Transform
your
Cooking

Transform *your* Cooking

*A Grace-Filled Guide
to Small Changes
with a* **Big Impact**
in Your Kitchen

Kelly Kauffman

Table of Contents

Introduction

Do you feel overwhelmed when it comes to feeding your family? Does it sometimes feel like you're getting by, but not really providing meals that you feel good about? There are so many choices in our grocery stores that we are often left feeling like we want to throw in the dish towel and order pizza, or head to the nearest fast food restaurant with golden arches and a drive-through. Navigating the aisles as we shop for food can be so discouraging. Reading recipes and food blogs can leave us feeling like we'll never be able to measure up. We've almost given up on cooking nutritious food—and we have to do it at least three times a day!

It doesn't have to be this way. What if I told you that you can feed your family well and not run yourself ragged in the process? What if I showed you how to make changes in small, easy to implement ways that left you feeling like you were doing the best for your children? What if you could learn to give yourself grace when you just can't "do it all?" That's what this book is all about.

I am not a doctor or healthcare practitioner. I am also not a food scientist. I am a wife and a mom of five precious kids. I make and serve three meals most days, as well as snacks, just like many of you. I have struggled, and still struggle, over what I should prepare for my family, as well as how to get everything done in the kitchen along with completing everything else I have on my plate—no pun intended!

Over the last decade, I have taken a journey to transform my cooking into something I can feel good about. It hasn't been easy. I've had a lot of disasters in the kitchen. By trying to do too much at once, I exhausted myself. I have given up and then tried again. Over the years, however, after many failures and flops, I have learned to cook and feed my family meals that I know will nourish and strengthen them and provide them with the energy they need to get through their day. I have learned that I don't have to do it perfectly and that imperfection is just fine. I have learned to give myself the same grace that I would give to others.

Since I have begun to make changes in my kitchen, the health of my family has greatly improved. We've only been to the doctor a handful of times. Those visits weren't even for sicknesses; we've had a broken bone, an infection from a newly pierced ear, a pocket knife accident that required stitches, and a few other similar incidents. Before our kitchen transformation, my family would suffer from strep throat at least once a year. Now, it has been over six years and we haven't even had one case of strep throat. In fact, my youngest two children, both born after our journey to transform our kitchen, have never taken an antibiotic in their lives. Don't get me wrong; we still get colds and viruses that put us out of commission for a few days, but they are short-lived and milder than in the past. Again, I am no doctor or scientist, so I don't know for sure why our level of illness has decreased so dramatically, but I know it seems to coincide with our kitchen changes.

So, while I can't promise that we'll never get sick—or that you'll never get sick—our experience has been rewarding and has saved time and money because we've avoided office visits to our family doctor.

If you are struggling to figure out what to feed your family that will be healthy and nourishing, the steps in this book will help. If you are intimidated by cooking, this book will make it painless. If you feel like you are not able to keep up with the "foodies" out there, this book will offer a realistic plan.

Transform Your Cooking is a guide to help you change your family's eating habits one tiny step at a time. It is completely guilt-free and full of grace. It is comfortable and simple. You will be able to easily implement these concepts as soon as you are ready and move at your own pace.

It has taken me many years to develop and gather these ideas. I have swung the pendulum from fanaticism—"I have to do it all, I have to do it perfectly and I have to do it now"—back to burnout—"I give up. I quit. Let's get fast food." Over time, however, I learned there's a better way. I don't have to live in either of those camps. I don't have to hold on to those expectations. I don't have to spend my entire day in the kitchen to feed my family the kind of foods that I can feel good about. I can give myself grace on days when going to the drive-through seems like the only option.

By implementing the ideas in this book, there is no question—you *will* have a healthier kitchen. You will not feel overwhelmed in the process. You will have less stress about what's for dinner, and your family will enjoy what you provide. You can let go of the guilt and the harsh demands you make of yourself. You will be able to serve breakfast, lunch, and dinner with confidence and a smile.

Do not continue to question whether you are doing all you can in the kitchen. Do not continue to feel overwhelmed when planning meals. Do not let the stress of trying to be perfect prevent you from providing your family with the best food you can. Rest assured, the steps provided in this book are easy to implement and will not leave you feeling overwhelmed. You will no longer feel like a failure in the kitchen and you will be successful in changing the way your family eats.

The concepts you are about to learn will encourage you, motivate you, and help you move toward a healthier lifestyle. You will not only change your meals, you will change the lives of your family. What are you waiting for? Turn the page and start transforming your cooking today!

Part One

Chapter 1
Why Should I Care?

Another day. I don't want to wake up in the morning and spend my entire day in the kitchen. Why does my family want to eat so much? And half of what I make, they pick at and complain about. I just can't do it anymore. But if I don't give them the best I can, their health will suffer. They won't be able to concentrate on their school work. They'll run out of energy before lunch time and maybe even fall asleep in the middle of an assignment. Fine. I'll make breakfast. What if I just make a homemade healthy breakfast? That's a good way to start the day, right? Surely their little bodies can handle a lunch of frozen chicken nuggets and a squeezable yogurt if they've started their day with something hearty and healthy.

But what if they can't handle it? What if those chicken nuggets have gluten? They weren't made from free range chickens. What if they have traces of antibiotics in them? And the yogurt? It has sugar! I'm not cut out for the cooking part of being a mom. I can't handle this. My kids will be lucky if they survive their childhood with all of this poison that I'm serving them! I don't know what to do. I don't have the energy to cook a three-course meal three times a day. Plus a snack. Don't forget the snacks. The kids will starve if they don't have three healthy snacks. They're always hungry. I can't fill them up. How am I going to feed my kids? How can I ever feel good about what I'm making for them?

Does this sound familiar? Have you ever felt like giving up because you can't do it perfectly? There's so much advice swirling around out there. Enough to make anyone feel like they've lost before they even start. So much of our society seems bent on shaming us, especially moms, for not doing things "the right way." And, the "right way" can be different depending on who you listen to. Many food blogs and dieting books send the message that if you don't follow their approach, you are messing up and destroying yourself and your family.

Advice like "eat only raw food," "avoid all food coloring," "drink your food by juicing it first," "eat only whole fruits and veggies," "carbs are awful and should always be avoided," "don't eat fat because it will make you fat," and "limit your protein" leaves us confused and wondering if there is anything safe to eat. There are so many expectations to be perfect that no one can keep up. We come out of the kitchen, throw our hands in the air, and tell our family to get in the car because we're going to get pizza. It's not worth trying if we have no chance of success, right? But *that's* what needs to change.

While we can find great ideas, scrumptious recipes, and new kitchen hacks by following popular foodies, we need to decide for ourselves what we can handle and how much time, effort, and money we have available for making changes in the kitchen. This will look different for every single family and that is okay. There is no list of rules that applies to everyone. There is no single path to good health. There is no right way to make stress-free meals. You must figure out what will work for you and your kitchen and let the rest go, at least for now. This is what I want to walk you through. In the upcoming chapters, I will help you sort through what is important to you and what you can realistically do to make some changes immediately. I will also show you how to set up a plan for the changes that you want to make eventually, when you are in the life stage that allows them, when you have the money available, and when you are ready for them.

Why is What We Eat Important?

Why should we care about what we eat and feed our families? Isn't the point to avoid hunger? Well, yes, that is one of the points. But it's not the only point, or even the most important point. We eat because our bodies need proper nutrition in order to function optimally. The food we eat should contain vitamins, minerals, enzymes, and other nutrients to properly nourish us. Without these important nutrients, our bodies will begin to slow down and break down. We will not be the best person we can be.

The Bible tells us that our body is a temple. As a Christian, my body is home to the Holy Spirit. I want to provide Him with the best home that I can. The Bible also tells me to be a good steward of the things for which God has given me responsibility. This includes our finances, our homes, and our other possessions, but it also includes our bodies. While it is true that our bodies are not eternal, and as Christians we know we will be receiving perfect, eternal bodies some day (Philippians 3:21), the body that we have right now has been entrusted to us for our time on earth and we should treat it with respect. In order to do this, we must care for it properly.

And, while we are speaking of being good stewards, the money we spend on food should be spent wisely. Convenience foods and eating out can be expensive. Don't misunderstand; I am in no way advocating for a strict lifestyle without fun treats, eating out, or easy shortcuts. Quite the opposite! I am saying we should make our choices carefully. Our body is fearfully and wonderfully made (Psalm 139:14) and can compensate for the times we choose less than optimal foods. But if we are doing this 100 percent of the time, our bodies will run out of resources. The body needs to have something to pull from so it can cover the times when we aren't giving it enough.

We also have our children to think about. It is our responsibility to take care of them the best we can. Our children are not our own. They, too, have been entrusted to our care and are a gift from God (Psalm 127:3). When God gave them to us it was because He trusted that we would be the best caretaker for them. It is our responsibility to help them be healthy. Just as we wouldn't purposely expose our children to a dangerous disease or sit back and watch them endanger themselves, we cannot approach our responsibility of providing them with meals lackadaisically, as if it has no impact or importance.

What our children eat when they are young can set them up for either good health or disease. It can also teach them patterns and habits that they may have a hard time breaking when they reach adulthood and begin making their own food choices. This is not to say that what we do when our children are young seals their future. Of course, having a solid foundation in the beginning makes the path easier for them as they grow, but it is never too late to change habits.

This should not add another layer of guilt or stress. If you are like me, you don't need any help with that. As you will soon see, this book is intended to help remove all feelings of guilt and stress when it comes to our kitchens. I merely bring these points up to help motivate you and give you reason to make changes toward a healthier home as you are able. If you get nothing else out of the time you spend reading this book, I hope that you embrace the idea of grace in the kitchen. Of course, this idea pertains to many areas of parenting and life in general, but the focus of this book is on our choices in the kitchen.

Priorities

Every one of us has been given the same amount of time. We have twenty-four hours in a day and seven days in a week. How we choose to spend this time varies from person to person. Some people enjoy being in the kitchen and make this a top priority. Others will find that cooking is not their favorite way to spend their time, but they still want to feel good about what they're making for their family. While it is still important to them, it is not as high on their list of priorities.

How much time and money you have and are willing to spend on food and preparing meals is something you will need to decide for yourself. If you have a larger budget and more time available, you will be able to make changes more quickly. However, if you are working a full-time job, helping children with various activities, and living on a tight budget, then your changes will need to come more slowly. Where you fall on this spectrum is highly individual. I cannot tell you whether you're doing enough or if you need to step up your game. That is something for you to decide for your own unique situation. Just remember, there is no wrong way (except maybe not trying at all). You live under grace. You are not subjected to a list of do's and don'ts. You have the freedom to do things differently than your neighbor or your best friend or your favorite food blogger. You need to do what works for you.

We cannot do all the things all the time. We must make choices. This pertains to all aspects of our lives, including in the kitchen. Each day will not look the same, either. One day we may be able to spend more time in the kitchen preparing and getting ahead because we know the next day we are going to be busy spending time in other areas of our life and we won't have as much time to dedicate to cooking tasks. And, to complicate it even more, this typically changes from week to week as we fill in our hours with work expectations, appointments, children's school activities, church functions, and all of the other requirements in our daily lives. Planning ahead will help you stay on top of the things you want to do in the kitchen. I will help walk you through how to do this. It won't be difficult, either.

Knowing that we will have busy days and busy seasons, we need to allow for compromises. There will be times when we can't do all the things we'd like to do in the kitchen. Even after you've learned, mastered, and implemented all the various ideas we'll talk about in this book, there will be times when you'll need to scale back what you can do. This is okay. Please allow yourself to do this and not feel guilty about it. As long as you are doing the best you can with the time you have for cooking tasks, that's all you should expect from yourself.

I fully believe that our relationships with our family and other loved ones should be much higher on everyone's list of priorities than the food we eat and serve. If I am busy with other activities I'm spending my time on, and still trying to have a perfect kitchen, I know I will feel overwhelmed. When I feel this way, it is much harder to be patient and understanding with the people I love the most, and this puts a strain on my relationships.

Stress is one of the main factors that leads to illness. If we are working too hard to make our kitchens perfect, and at the same time exhausting ourselves on other tasks, it's just not worth it. I believe the stress we often cause ourselves by trying to do too much and worrying over whether we are inadvertently harming our children by serving them a subpar meal does a lot more damage than just happily eating the food we are worried about. It is not healthy for our bodies to live in a constant state of stress. With mealtimes coming around three times a day and snacks in between, there's plenty of opportunity to let this happen if we are not careful.

Finding Balance

We must find a balance. Everyone's schedules, priorities, budgets, interests, and tastes vary. There is no one-size-fits-all plan for serving your family healthy meals. However, spending too much time on either side of the spectrum—from 100 percent homemade, from scratch, whole, organic foods made with the perfect cooking techniques to 100 percent sugar-filled, empty calorie, pre-made junk food—will not be healthy, either. One side may lead to burnout and stress, and the other could lead to health-related problems, obesity, and general feelings of malaise.

Most likely, you will fall somewhere between these two extremes on any given day. There will be periods of time when you may find yourself closer to one end or another for a while. Once life demands something different, or priorities change, you must be willing to change your approach to cooking. If this means you need to swing toward the "less healthful" end of the spectrum for a time, then so be it. Do what you need to do for that instance, then re-evaluate and move back toward the center or even further.

We have to be realistic when we are planning meals and serving our family. We must take into consideration many things that will affect how much we can do in the kitchen. Our budgets need to be consulted. There may be times when you cannot afford to buy organic produce and grass-fed beef. Do the best you can with the money you have. Do not go into debt to buy food that you cannot really afford! You may also not be able to buy certain appliances or tools that would allow you to more easily prepare foods in healthful ways. Make a savings plan and work toward it. In the meantime, purchase the best options that you can get.

We also must take into account our schedules. If you have young children who demand your attention during all of their waking hours, this is probably not the best time to try to learn a bunch of new cooking skills in a week and implement them all by the next weekend. Or, if your children are teenagers and hungry all their waking hours and just can't seem to ever be filled up, you may find you don't have enough hours in a day to make enough foods and snacks. Take it slow and easy! This is not a race. Any positive changes toward a healthy kitchen will make a difference.

The Bible warns over and over about the dangers of taking an idol for worship (Exodus 3:4-5, Philippians 3:19). I have seen myself and others fall into a pattern where we have made food an idol. I wasn't bowing down and singing or praying to my bread, but I put such a high importance on making sure that my food was prepared in a certain way or bought from a certain place or grown using a certain method that I lost sight of my reasons for even wanting to be healthy—so that I can serve God and others to the best of my abilities.

The quest for health for myself and my family began to take first place in my life. I had squeezed God completely out of the kitchen and tried to control it all myself. After completely burning myself out, driving my family crazy, and feeling convicted by God, I realized that I needed to make changes. I needed to learn to loosen up and trust that God would give me the grace to do just what I could do at that time in my life, no more and no less. He gave me the freedom to not be perfect. Once I embraced this, I gave myself a lot more slack. I allowed myself to purchase some convenience foods and to make some compromises in my grocery shopping. And I felt so much better!

My family's health has not suffered from these decisions. I have more time to spend with the people I care about, and the feeling of being overwhelmed has dissipated. *These* changes have been healthier and more freeing than the strict and rigid rules I had initially placed on myself and my family in my search for health. What started out as a good thing—a way to honor God by trying to provide Him the best temple I could and to raise children to want to do the same—turned into an idol, something I put above Him. And I was teaching this to my children through my actions, as well.

I do believe God expects us to do our best and try our hardest with the resources He has graciously given us (1 Corinthians 10:31). He will handle everything else. We must rest in our faith that God will provide for our needs and all we can do is walk obediently, trusting Him each step of the way. Pray over your food, dedicate your day and your time to fulfilling what He has planned for you, and know that He has everything under control, even when it feels like our kitchen (and sometimes our whole lives) are in complete chaos and falling apart. It will all be okay in the end, Mama.

Throughout the rest of the book, I will give you tips and steps that will help transform your cooking. Please remember that what I have done will most likely be different than what you are going to do. What has worked for me may not work for you because we have different schedules, come from different financial situations, have different priorities, and like different things. Please do not become rigid about implementing any of the ideas in this book, and if you begin to feel overwhelmed, please step back a little. Don't try to implement too many changes at once. Take everything gradually and rest assured that you are making positive changes in your home and you and your family will benefit from whatever you can manage.

There is no set order to follow with these steps. I advise you to read through everything and start with the areas that seem the least intimidating and the most doable. Set yourself up for success. I will let you know the order in which I implemented our changes, but feel free to jump around, skip steps, come back and pick something up later that you may have chosen to avoid for now.

As you learn a new technique, you may have to scale back a little on other areas that you have already implemented. That's completely fine. Once you feel comfortable, you will know when to add something you've set aside or add something completely different. Just never forget to give yourself the same grace that God offers you and don't let yourself get to the point that you're ready to quit altogether. You can do this. I'm excited to join you on a journey that will change your life!

Chapter 2
Tools of the Trade

We are fortunate to live in a time when we have many helpers in the kitchen. Gone are the days when cooks had to light and stoke a fire in order to boil water or cook food. We no longer have to churn our own butter or slaughter our own chickens. We have the blessing of electricity and the invention of stoves, ovens, and refrigerators. There are many other kitchen appliances and gadgets we can purchase that make our jobs so much easier. These will shave hours off of our time in the kitchen.

There are also many frivolous items you probably won't use often enough to justify the purchase. You don't need much in order to have a well-stocked, fully-functioning kitchen. In fact, if you have too much in your kitchen, it can slow you down; you'll spend time hunting for the exact tool you need for the job. Having just the basics, plus the extra things you really love and use, will help you streamline your kitchen and use your time more efficiently.

I will list several items that I consider essential, and then I will discuss others that are just nice to have. Most of the items I consider necessary are relatively inexpensive, and if you've done any cooking you probably have some of them already. However, several of the optional items are more expensive, and you may need to make a plan in order to save for them.

I use my optional items just as much, if not more, than some of the required tools. I highly recommend trying to save for them if you are serious about changing your kitchen. They will make your life as family cook so much easier. The reason they are listed as optional, rather than necessary, is because you can create the same meals without them. It will just take more effort or time without these tools. You can view a list of the items I use in my kitchen by visiting *homeandfaith.com/resources*.

So, let's get started with the tools that I consider requirements. I list these in no particular order because they are all equally important.

Knives

The first item is a set of good quality, sharp knives. It is so important that your knives are sharp! A dull knife is actually more dangerous than a sharp knife. It can slip off the item you are cutting much easier. You have to push so much harder on a dull knife in order to get it to slice through the food. These two factors become an accident waiting to happen. It is worth it to have sharp knives in your kitchen. If your knives are no longer sharp, please take them to be sharpened. Many butcher counters in local grocery stores will offer this service for free. It is often not advertised. They already keep sharpeners on site so their blades are always sharp. It is worth it to stop by the counter of the meat department in your local grocery store and inquire as to whether they offer this service.

If you decide to purchase new knives and don't want to spend the money on an entire set all at once, there are some knives that are more versatile than others. The knives I use most commonly include a butcher knife, a paring knife, a five-inch all-purpose knife, and a serrated bread knife. I prefer the Santoku-style knives because I like their flat blades. This is a personal preference.

I use a butcher knife to slice and cut various meats. I use the paring knife when I am chopping or dicing small items, such as a piece of onion or herbs. The small blade allows you to be more precise. The five-inch all-purpose knife is probably my most commonly used knife. It can slice cheese, cut through apples, and chop potatoes.

The serrated bread knife is a must once you begin making breads—both quick and yeast breads. It is able to cut slices of bread without tearing through them or squashing the loaf. I also use the serrated knife to slice tomatoes. The serrated blade makes it easier to cut through the skin and slice the softer inside without smashing the tomato.

If you are shopping for new knives, look for a durable knife. The steel of the blade should extend through the length of the handle. I have bought cheaper knives and had the blade break off at the handle. It is definitely worth it to spend the extra money and have a longer-lasting knife.

Cutting Boards

Along with your knives, you will also need cutting boards. I use several different kinds in my kitchen. I have a bamboo cutting board that I think is pretty enough to leave out on my counter. I mostly use this one to cut bread and other dry items since it is not as easy to sanitize. I have a couple of rigid plastic cutting boards and a few flexible cutting boards, as well. If I am chopping something that I will be scraping into a bowl, I use the flexible plastic boards because I can roll the edges up to fit inside the bowl as I'm scraping the pieces in once I'm done cutting. This helps to keep the mess to a minimum as it guides the food into the bowl. Plastic boards can be put into your soapy dishwater and sanitized easily. They are not expensive and will save your countertops from nicks and dings as well as help to keep your knife blades sharper.

Baking Pans, Pots, and Muffin Tins

Other necessary items for your kitchen are baking pans, pots, and muffin tins. I do not typically buy pans with nonstick Teflon coating anymore. They kept peeling, and bits of the coating ended up in our food. I now use stainless steel pots with a bit of oil in the bottom to keep things from sticking or I use seasoned cast iron pots.

I use pans that have a coating of silicone on them, or I add a silicone mat on top of a regular baking sheet to prevent items from sticking. I also use muffin tins that are coated with silicone or reusable silicone muffin liners. For glass pans, I use an oil mister and spray olive or avocado oil on them to keep the food from sticking to them.

The most commonly used pots and pans in my kitchen include a small saucepan and a medium saucepan, cookie sheets and muffin tins, and casserole dishes. I have several half sheet pans that I use for cookie sheets as well as a quarter sheet pan. I have three 9- by 13-inch casserole dishes. Two are glass and one is aluminized steel with silicone coating. I have two regular sized muffin tins; each holds twelve muffins. My mini muffin tin makes twenty-four cute little muffins.

Cookie Scoops

A very useful tool that will pair nicely with your muffin tins and cookie sheets is a cookie scoop. This is not a necessity, as you can just use a spoon to make your cookies or muffins, but it makes the job a lot quicker and smoother. I have multiple sizes. I use a large cookie scoop that holds three tablespoons and a medium-sized one that holds one and a half tablespoons. The larger one measures the perfect amount for a regular size muffin, and it can also be used to make large cookies. I use the medium-sized one for mini muffins or a regular size cookie. It is also used frequently in my house to make energy bites or meatballs. These are very handy little tools.

Mixing Bowls

Mixing bowls are requirements. I have two glass mixing bowls—a small (four-cup capacity) and a large (eight-cup capacity). These both have lips on them and are perfect for mixing batters or other recipes that you will be pouring into another pan. I also have three nesting stainless steel bowls. These have heavy bottoms and do not slide around on my counter. I would recommend having at least three bowls of various sizes to start with.

Mixing Spoons and Spatulas

You will also want wooden or silicone spoons and a silicone spatula to stir and mix ingredients. Make sure that the spoons you use can sustain high temperatures so that you can use them to stir food that is heating on the stovetop. A flexible silicone spatula that can be used with high temperatures will be indispensable when you need to transfer sticky, thick dough or batter to other pans. The spatula will help scrape the bowl clean, leaving less waste behind and giving you a head start on your cleanup!

Measuring Cups and Spoons

The last necessary things you will need to have a functional kitchen are measuring cups and measuring spoons. A simple set of metal or plastic measuring spoons is fine to measure one fourth teaspoon, one half teaspoon, one teaspoon, and one tablespoon. You will also need plastic or metal measuring cups that include one fourth cup, one third cup, one half cup, and one cup. These are used to measure dry ingredients, such as flour, sugar, or oats. Measuring cups with a lip are also needed. I have a one cup, two cup, and a four cup glass measuring cup. Plastic cups are fine, but glass will last longer. These are used to measure liquid ingredients like water or oil.

That wraps up the basic list of required tools you will need in your kitchen. You probably already have most, if not all of these, unless you have never really cooked before. Now we'll move on to the more fun, but entirely optional tools. I highly recommend each of the items on this list. I use most of them weekly, some two or three times a week. While you can make the same recipes without these items, having them will greatly reduce your time in the kitchen and make your cooking time easier and more enjoyable. Most of them are somewhat expensive, however, so if you are interested in adding these to your kitchen, make a savings plan and save up for them. Make a wish list and purchase them as you can afford them. Again, I have listed the exact items I use on *homeandfaith.com/resources*.

Grain Mill

The first thing I recommend, which I believe is the most important and will make a big impact on your family's health, is an electric grain mill. I know this sounds really strange. Perhaps you have never even heard of such an appliance. It is a simple tool to use and will add immensely to your baking and cooking projects. A good grain mill will cost you somewhere in the $200 range.

A grain mill is an appliance that takes whole grains and grinds them into a flour. You can take whole wheat berries, completely intact with the bran still on them, and dump them into the mill. The mill will grind them and shoot the resulting flour into a container. It is mess-free and hands-free (other than turning it on and off). It's no harder than measuring out a cup of all-purpose flour that you can buy at the store. Instead of measuring flour, you will measure grains. We will talk about this technique in chapter six, which is dedicated to grains.

A grain mill can grind most grains into flour, like wheat, corn, popcorn, and rice. It cannot grind oily or fatty things like nuts or seeds. When you purchase your grain mill, it will include a list of items it can and cannot grind. I cannot stress enough how valuable this one appliance is to improving your health and the health of your family. You will absolutely not regret saving for it and purchasing it. If you truly want to push your family toward a healthier diet, this is one of the easiest and most rewarding purchases you can make.

Pressure Cooker

A close second to the grain mill is an electric pressure cooker. This little appliance has revolutionized my kitchen! A pressure cooker can cook meals in a fraction of the time they would normally cook in the oven or on the stove. You put your ingredients into the cooker, set the timer and pressure level according to the directions in the recipe and walk away. There is no need to babysit the cooker or to check on its contents. In fact, once the pressure cooker has built up the pressure, you *cannot* check the contents. The lid will be locked on.

If you have heard horror stories of pressure cookers exploding and leaving sauce covered holes in kitchen ceilings, you can put that fear aside. Today's electric pressure cookers are much safer than the cookers your grandmother used. They have multiple safety features in place and will automatically release pressure if the pressure begins to build too high. You literally can walk out of the kitchen and let the cooker make your dinner.

My pressure cooker has a slow cooker mode, a yogurt mode, a rice cooker mode, and several other handy functions. I have replaced multiple appliances and saved precious space in my kitchen with this one appliance. I probably use it equally as often as a pressure cooker and as a slow cooker. It works well as both and both functions are indispensable if you are looking to save time and sanity in the kitchen. If you are new to pressure cooking, you may want a good cookbook dedicated to cooking with a pressure cooker. I have listed my favorites on *homeandfaith.com/resources*.

The techniques you can use are different than stovetop, oven, or slow cooking. It is not hard to use an electric pressure cooker; it is just different. I have a couple of recipes that use the electric pressure cooker in various sections in the next part of the book to get you started. A good electric pressure cooker will cost about $100, but when you take into account the number of appliances it can replace, and the time you will save, this is actually a really good deal.

Bread Machine

The next appliance I use on a regular basis is a good bread machine. As you will read in later chapters, one of the easiest ways to quickly improve your family's health is through the breads that you serve them. You can make bread for your family, and it doesn't have to be hard! As you probably know, making bread from scratch can be time consuming. With a bread machine, however, you can get most of that time back.

All you have to do is dump the ingredients into the pan and push a few buttons. In a few hours, you'll have a delicious loaf of bread. Or you can set it to make the dough for you, and then use the dough to shape a variety of baked goods like rolls, pizza, and small loaves of bread. Owning a bread machine will help make having healthy breads in your home on a regular basis much more doable. I will go into more depth on breads in later chapters. Plan on spending between $60 and $250 for a good machine.

Mixers

A mixer is another useful tool that you might consider adding to your arsenal. A hand mixer can be found at most department stores and is relatively inexpensive. For most jobs, this is probably all you need. It is nice to have a mixer when making cookies, cakes, and other sweets. I also use it to make mashed potatoes. It is much easier than trying to mix stiff ingredients together by hand. If you find that you often have larger jobs, like several loaves of bread or a large batch of cookies, you may want to invest in a stand mixer that sits on your countertop. The bowls that come with stand mixers hold a bigger quantity and the power is stronger, so it can mix more at one time than a hand mixer.

A blender is also nice to have. I don't use my blender often and have not invested in one of the super powerful blenders that can blend anything. I have not found that I need it often enough to invest a lot of money in a blender. I do use a blender to make simple smoothies for my children for breakfast. We don't make these on a daily basis and I don't typically add ingredients that are tough to blend, so I feel like we don't need a top-of-the-line blender. If you want to make smoothies on a regular basis, or add lots of greens to your smoothie, then a higher quality blender would be beneficial. Otherwise, a cheaper blender will probably suit you best.

Food Processor

A food processor ranks pretty high on my list of useful appliances. I use my food processor often. If you decide to get a food processor, please make sure it comes with a shredding attachment. I buy blocks of cheese and run them through the food processor. In less than ten seconds, I have shredded cheese with no added ingredients. I also use the food processor to make pie crust, chop nuts, make salsa, make nut butters, and many more things. You will find a few recipes in later sections that utilize the food processor. A good food processor costs anywhere from $50 to $200.

Salad Spinner

Another simple tool is a salad spinner. These are inexpensive and make serving fresh salads easier. Just add your greens to the colander, rinse them thoroughly and then spin them. The water is removed and you have fresh, crisp, clean lettuce as a base for your salads. Having simple tools like this helps to ensure that you will serve these types of healthy foods to your family. You can get a salad spinner for between $10 and $30.

I will discuss the last three tools together since I typically use them together. A pastry mat, a rolling pin, and a bench scraper make it easier to work with dough and make the cleanup so much faster. These are all relatively inexpensive. A pastry mat is a silicone mat that lays on your countertop. It typically has various measurements on it. Mine has rulers along the edges and a series of concentric circles in the middle. The circles help when rolling out dough for pizzas or pies. If you want a nine-inch pie crust, just roll your dough to fit inside the nine-inch circle.

I have a traditional rolling pin, but the one I use more often is a handheld pin that has a roller at each end—one smaller than the other. I find this type easier to manage and work with. A bench scraper is a tool that is used to cut through larger chunks of dough to divide it into the appropriate number of pieces. It is easier to use than a knife because it is bigger and can cut through more of the dough with one straight cut. For example, I use this to divide a lump of dough into sixteen smaller pieces for dinner rolls. The bench scraper just makes this job easier. The biggest bonus to the pastry mat and bench scraper is the ease of cleanup. When you are done with your dough, just carefully roll the pastry mat and carry it to your sink. *Voila!* Your countertops are clean. If you do happen to get flour or dough stuck to your counter, use your bench scraper to scrape it off and carry it to your sink. A quick swipe with a cleaning rag and your counters are as good as new.

You may have other tools that you use and love. That's fine! You should continue to use them. But if you have a lot of extra gizmos and gadgets that never see the light of day, consider donating them or at least boxing them up and moving them somewhere else to see if you can live without them. I think you will find your kitchen is a much happier place to work in if you just stick with the things you use regularly. I have found it worthwhile to invest in having nice, sometimes more expensive, appliances that work well.

The things that make my job easier and save me time are the appliances I use on a regular basis. If I can make a cooking job easy, I will be so much more likely to actually do it. If a meal is going to take me two hours of hands-on time to prepare, then it probably won't happen. I either won't plan it at all, or I'll plan it and then decide that evening to change the plans and just order pizza or go out. So, knowing the job is actually doable with my current schedule and responsibilities means I will be more likely to follow through and get it done.

Chapter 3
So What Can I Eat?

There are so many diets out there today and so many different opinions about what is healthy and what is not. So many people have allergies and intolerances in numbers that seem to be growing every day. Some supposed "health experts" tell us to avoid whole food groups, or advise us to only eat this certain type of food as long it is combined with that other type of food in the same meal and never combine it with this other type of food. Oh, and make sure you always buy fat free, or at the very least, low fat foods! There is so much hype surrounding gluten right now that you almost feel sick if you so much as glance at a piece of white bread. It's so confusing, and all of the contradictions and misinformation can leave us paralyzed when it comes to making decisions about what foods are safe for our family.

If you or a family member have allergies or intolerances, then please do the wise thing and avoid those foods! However, if that is not the case, there's really no reason to exclude a food, and especially not a whole food group, unless you personally do not enjoy that food. Let's start by defining what I mean by food and food groups.

My broad definition of food is something that we consume that gives us energy and supplies our body with nourishment. When I refer to a food group, I am talking about the categories that were listed on old food pyramids—dairy, grains, fruits, vegetables, and fats. All of these food groups provide nutrients that are necessary for an optimally functioning body. By excluding or extremely limiting one or more food groups, you are depriving your body of vitamins, minerals, or other important nutrients that it needs. There are ways to work around this if you have allergies or if you are a vegetarian. That is not the scope of this book, however.

Foods are broken down into what are called macronutrients and micronutrients. Micronutrients include vitamins, minerals, and enzymes. For the rest of this chapter, we will concentrate on three main macronutrients, as these seem to be the causes of concern and the focus of many of the popular diets today. Don't worry, this will be a very basic primer on macronutrients and will not delve deep or use a lot of hard-to-understand scientific jargon.

The three main macronutrients are carbohydrates, proteins, and fats. It is important to know about these because, in understanding their primary functions and purposes, you will understand why it is necessary to consume all three. Without one, your diet will be unbalanced and you will have negative effects at some point. God created our food. He has given us good things to eat. Yes, we have manipulated and changed some of God's creations and can now create new foods in a lab with chemicals. However, the foods that God has given us to consume are good for us. He created carbohydrates, proteins, and fats. He put them together in just the right ratios. Unless you or a family member truly reacts to certain foods, it is not wise to leave them out of your diet. God knew what He was doing when He created our bodies and when He created the food to sustain them.

Carbohydrates

The first macronutrient, and the one that seems to be getting the most press recently, is carbohydrates. Carbohydrates, or carbs, are found in grains, vegetables, and even fruits. They are essential for creating energy and providing fiber. Carbs break down into sugar—primarily glucose. Our body requires glucose to function. Without it, we will die. It is the main energy source for the brain and the body's cells. Glucose is a form of sugar into which carbs are broken down. There are two types of carbs—complex carbs and simple carbs.

Simple Carbohydrates

Simple carbs are called simple because they are made up of simple molecules of glucose, fructose, or other sugars. They are digested and broken down very quickly into individual sugar molecules, converted to glucose, and absorbed directly into the blood stream through the small intestine. Simple sugars are foods like ordinary table sugar, fruits, honey, syrups, and even milk and yogurt.

Table sugar contains only molecules of simple carbs and breaks down very quickly. This is why eating candies and sweets that contain a lot of sugar gives us an energy rush quickly after consuming them. The downside, however, is that after we eat this and get a rush of blood sugar, our body sends a large amount of insulin to help distribute and clean up all this excess sugar. The insulin does its job so well that we're soon left with blood sugar levels that are even lower than they were to begin with. This can make us feel sluggish and lethargic, or even shaky and lightheaded.

Fruits, honey, and milk do not create this problem as easily because, along with sugar molecules, they contain other nutrients. These other nutrients can help the body digest and use the sugars in a way that doesn't leave us as prone to the spikes and dips that table sugar can cause.

Complex Carbohydrates

Complex carbs are called complex because they are made of longer strands of sugar molecules that break down more slowly. These include foods such as whole grains, beans, and vegetables. As the body uses enzymes to digest and break down these carbs, they are turned into simple sugars. These simple sugars are then absorbed into the bloodstream. Because these carbs are complex, they do not break down as quickly as simple carbs. This longer-lasting digestion helps to prevent some of the problems we may encounter with simple sugars.

Fiber

If pastas and breads are made from whole grain, they also provide fiber and other micronutrients to the body. The fiber and other nutrients help in the digestive process and regulate how quickly the glucose is used and dispersed. It helps your body absorb nutrients. Insoluble fiber is not digested like sugars. It is used to clean the intestines. Insoluble fiber works almost like a broom, sweeping the intestines clean. It helps to move the food through the digestive tract. Without adequate fiber intake, partially digested food from the stomach may spend too much time in the intestinal tract. Whole grains and vegetables prevent this from happening and are essential for proper digestion and elimination of waste.

It is important to try to include whole grains into your diet. I believe that much of the hype surrounding the consumption of grain has more to do with the fact that our society eats a lot of refined white flours. They're not getting all the other benefits that come with eating whole grains. A diet consisting only of white flours may eventually cause sugar imbalances or other problems. However, a diet rich with whole grains will be easier on the body, nutritious, and full of benefits. When refined white flours are traded for whole grains and white sugar for nutritious sweeteners, such as honey, I believe many of the problems most diets claim are caused by grains will disappear.

Many people do not like the thought of trading white bread for whole wheat bread or giving up sugar. There are ways to make these changes and still like your foods, though. I will be walking you through these topics as we progress. Please do not give up. The whole grains you have probably been exposed to in the past are not what I'm talking about. I'm not going to tell you to start buying bags of whole wheat flour from the store instead of white flour. I don't like that, either. I feel it creates a bad taste and an unpleasant texture in baked goods. I can understand why people would rather give up flour altogether before switching to store-bought whole wheat flour.

The techniques and recipes I will share with you will taste just as good, or better, than the foods you are used to. And, remember, you will make these changes gradually and simply. You absolutely do not have to give up your favorite treats, even those made with white sugar. They just need to have an appropriate place in your life.

As you can see, carbohydrates play a very important role in our diet. Please do not exclude or severely limit your carb intake. It will not be healthy, and it will cause problems for you. You may need to make some slow, small changes to your diet and the meals you serve your family in order to improve the carbs you prepare, but it will not be overwhelming. It will be easy; I promise. If you have gluten sensitivities, you can still enjoy gluten-free grains and starches so you'll be consuming enough carbs to provide your body with the energy it requires.

Proteins

The next macronutrient we will focus on is protein. Proteins are present in every single living cell. Protein provides energy and is necessary for growth, especially in children and pregnant women. It helps create lean muscle mass and repair tissue. It does most of the work in our cells.

Proteins are made of strings of amino acids. There are twenty different types of amino acids used in our bodies that come together in different combinations to make proteins. Our bodies can make some amino acids; however, there are nine which the human body cannot manufacture. These nine amino acids are called the essential amino acids. We must get these from our diet.

Proteins that come from animal sources, such as beef, chicken, and dairy foods, contain all nine essential amino acids, making them a good addition to your diet. Proteins from animal sources are called complete proteins since they contain all nine amino acids.

Protein is found in plants, as well. However, they are incomplete proteins, meaning they do not contain all nine essential amino acids. Different plants have different amino acids and must be combined in order to form a complete protein. For example, rice and beans form a complete protein. It is not necessary to have complete proteins at a single meal. They can be spread throughout the day over several meals.

Protein molecules are complex molecules, and therefore take longer to break down in the digestive process. Because of this, proteins provide a slower and longer-lasting form of energy than carbohydrates. Many diets today emphasize proteins over carbs. And, while protein is a source of energy, it should not be your only source. Proteins do not break down into glucose. And, as mentioned earlier, glucose is necessary for the brain! Do not try to replace carbs with more protein.

Fats

The final macronutrient is fat. For so long, fat has been a bad word. There is a common misconception that including fats in our diets will make us become fat. So, a push for low-fat or fat free foods has become extremely popular. Sadly, this is not the answer to our weight issues. Low-fat and fat free foods are not healthier for us. When food manufacturers remove the fat, they must replace it with something else that will enhance the flavor. Often, it is replaced with sugar or corn syrup. As you have already read, these are carbohydrates, not fat. A manufacturer can remove the fat, replace it with sugar, and truthfully claim it is fat free. However, remember that eating excess sugar which the body cannot use quickly will be turned to glucose and stored in the fat cells. Fat cells can continue to stretch to accommodate the body's storage needs. Eating low fat or fat-free foods will not help in the long run if you're trying to lose weight.

Is the answer just to return to full fat foods? Well, the answer to that is, "That depends." The important thing to know about fats is that there are healthy fats and unhealthy fats. We do not want to include the unhealthy fats in our diets very often. It is very easy to switch the fats we use in our kitchens to healthier fats when we're cooking.

Like carbohydrates, fats are broken down into two main types. There are saturated fats and unsaturated fats. Saturated fats are called this because they are saturated with hydrogen molecules. These fats are usually solid at room temperature. Most come from animal sources. Some examples are beef, cheese, and butter. Coconut oil and palm oil are some exceptions. These are saturated fats from plant sources.

Unsaturated fats are not saturated with hydrogen molecules. They are typically liquid at room temperature and come from plant sources. Some examples of unsaturated fat sources include olive oil, some nuts, and avocados.

From here, it gets slightly more complicated, but I'll try to break it down so it's still easy to understand. Unsaturated fats are broken down into three main types: monounsaturated fats, polyunsaturated fats, and trans fats. Let's take a brief look at each of these types.

Monounsaturated Fats

Monounsaturated fats have one unsaturated chemical bond. These are typically liquid fats at room temperature, but they will begin to solidify when cold. Some examples are olive oil and coconut oil. Eggs, avocados, and almonds also contain saturated fat.

Polyunsaturated Fats

Polyunsaturated fats have multiple unsaturated chemical bonds. These fats are typically liquid at room temperature and stay liquid, even when refrigerated. Some examples are sunflower, corn, and soybean oils. Many nuts and seeds are also sources of polyunsaturated fats. Polyunsaturated fats include omega-3 and omega-6 oils. Many foods today contain a large amount of omega-6 oils and a much lower amount of omega-3 oils. Our bodies need close to equal ratios of omega-6 and omega-3 oils. Our diets today often make this hard to achieve.

Trans Fats

Trans fats are the third type of fats prevalent in our diets, although they are becoming less common. Most of them are artificially produced. They are created by adding hydrogen to vegetable oils. This process helps to make the liquid oils more solid. Most trans fats in our foods are called partially hydrogenated oils. Trans fats are found in many processed, fried, and baked foods. They were deemed unsafe by the Food and Drug Administration in 2013, and companies have been required to phase them out of their products by 2018.

Foods made or altered in a factory contain artificial ingredients, may have trans fats, and are not the same as the foods God gave us to eat. Switching to fats that come from plant sources, like coconut oil, olive oil, and palm oil is an easy change. Butter is a wonderful fat from an animal source that can be used instead of margarine. Many vegetable oils are rancid by the time they hit the store shelves. They are highly unstable. Olive oil or avocado oil are good examples of liquid oils that are more stable. There is no need to become stressed out over this, because these are easy changes to make. We will discuss how to use healthy oils and how to easily make these changes during the chapter on fats.

It should be obvious at this point that all three macronutrients are vitally important and necessary to a well-balanced and healthy diet. They fulfill different requirements, and one will not serve as an adequate replacement for another. You must have an adequate amount of all three. This will probably go against what you have read in many popular dieting books on the market today. But God created our food, and He did it perfectly. He did not intend for us to ignore whole groups of food. They all work together, like different sections of an orchestra, to nourish our bodies and provide good health.

Please remember that the information in this book is not here to make you feel guilty or worried about your food choices. Do not run to your kitchen and gather up every bag of white flour and sugar, and all your bottles of various oils, and throw them out. Don't try to change too many things all at once. If you are serious about making your kitchen healthier, it will all come in time. You do not need to panic or rush. Continue using what you have until you have determined that it's time to change it. Little by little, one item at a time, you will transform your cooking.

Chapter 4
The Nuts and Bolts
of Meal Planning

One of the easiest and best things you can do to help ensure you have healthy food on your table for your family that you can feel good about is to plan ahead. Making a meal plan is not hard, and it does not need to be restrictive, either. If I do not make a plan ahead of time, then I will be scrambling at 4:30 in the afternoon to figure out what we'll have for dinner. Most likely I won't have the ingredients on hand that I need, and we'll end up going out to eat.

It doesn't take long to plan meals, and it will definitely save you time in the kitchen once it comes to preparing them. You will already know what you'll be making and you'll have the ingredients on hand. By having a meal plan, you will also save money.

Meal Planning Styles

There are many different ways to make a meal plan. If you are new to meal planning, you may want to experiment with different approaches to find the one that suits you best. You may find that different styles work better for you during different seasons.

Weekly Meal Planning

One way to plan your meals is to plan what you'll eat for the next week. Plan all three meals and all snacks, even if your family packs a lunch to take with them. This will help you organize your shopping list to make sure you don't forget anything needed for packing lunches or making dinner. Often, I find myself providing the same things for breakfast and lunch if I don't take the time to plan them out ahead of time. Planning breakfasts and lunches ahead of time will ensure that there is a variety of different foods available for these meals. Planning for a week doesn't take as long, but must be redone every week. This is how I typically plan.

Monthly Meal Planning

Another common way to plan is for the whole month. At the end of the current month, sit down and take a while to plan all the meals for the upcoming month. Again, make a plan for all meals and snacks. Many people like this approach because they don't have to do it as often. However, it does take more time in one sitting. A way to make this a little easier is to have a breakfast and lunch rotation. Plan one or two weeks' worth of breakfasts and lunches and repeat them. This way, you're not starting from scratch every time you plan meals. You can do this with dinners, too, but my family and I like a little more variety with our evening meal, so I leave this more open-ended.

Seasonal Meal Planning

A third way to plan is seasonally. This helps you take advantage of fruits and vegetables in their peak harvesting time each season. Seasonal meal plans typically revolve around the freshest produce available during that time, and helps to ensure that you're including fruits and vegetables in your meals when they're at their tastiest and also at their cheapest. You can still include these in your meal plans if you are planning for a shorter length of time, but planning seasonally enables you to get a lot done ahead of time, while knowing you will have in-season fresh fruits and veggies on your table.

Shopping day to day is not recommended because it will take a lot more of your time as you drive to and from the store and spend time navigating the aisles over and over. It will also cost more because you will be more likely to add extra items to your cart as you'll be tempted more often. Going into the store once a week with a list in hand helps keep those extra splurges at bay. Just stick to the list. Get in and get out.

To begin a meal planning session, you will need your calendar. You can either add your plans directly to your calendar or write them on a separate meal planning sheet. For a free sheet to use to plan your meals, visit my website at *homeandfaith.com*. Begin by checking appointments and tasks scheduled for the days ahead in your meal planning cycle. Then you'll know how much time you will have in the kitchen and when you'll have it.

If you have a busy afternoon and won't be returning until right before it's time to sit down to dinner, then you can plan a meal for your slow cooker. Throw everything in the slow cooker in the morning and let it do the work during the day. When you come home, dinner will be ready and waiting. If the opposite is true and you have a busy morning, you could plan a meal for your pressure cooker in the afternoon or plan an easy, thirty-minute meal that you can put together in the evening. Knowing what your other obligations are prior to meal planning will make your plans easier to implement and less stressful because you'll be able to do the bulk of your prep work during less busy times of the day. If you know you will be eating out or going to a church picnic or some other activity for a meal, add this to your plan, too.

One very helpful technique to use when deciding what meals to prepare is to have theme nights. For example, Mondays can be pasta nights. Tuesdays can be Mexican food. Wednesdays can be reserved for trying out new recipes. Thursdays can be comfort food night. And, on Fridays, you can have pizza or grilled food. These are just examples. You can use these examples on nights that work for you or you can come up with entirely different themes.

Do whatever works for you and your schedule and choose food that your family enjoys and will eat. Using this technique helps narrow down the possibilities. Rather than limitless options for any given night, you can focus on a pasta recipe, for example. You don't have to have a different recipe for every single week, either. If you have Mexican food on Tuesdays, and your family loves tacos like mine does, then plan tacos for every other Tuesday and fill the opposite weeks with burritos, enchiladas, or some other Mexican dish. I try not to plan the same meal week after week. In my house, a beloved food can quickly become picked over if it returns to their plates too often. However, a couple of weeks in between seems the right amount of space to keep my family happy and anticipating their favorites.

Now you are ready to begin gathering recipes and recording your meal ideas on paper or on your computer. You may already know some meals that you can add to your plan right away. To fill in the others, just flip through books looking for recipes that meet your theme, if you're using one, and your time schedule.

When you find recipes online that you want to try, save them somewhere. If you use Evernote or OneNote, make a folder for recipes. You can also make a board on Pinterest for saving recipes. You can print them out and save them in a three-ring binder, as well. It doesn't matter how you do it, just save them somewhere. If you don't, you won't remember them. Look through your saved recipes to add to your meal plan.

Creating a Shopping List from Your Meal Plan

As you add recipes to your meal plan, add the ingredients to a shopping list. Don't forget to shop your own kitchen first. I have gone to the grocery store many times and come home with boxes of noodles or blocks of cheese that I already had in my pantry or refrigerator. I eventually use them up, but in the meantime I have to use valuable space in my kitchen to store them, and I did not need to spend money on them at that time.

When I am writing a shopping list, I divide my page into sections. I have a section for produce, one for dairy and refrigerated items, one for frozen foods, and one for dry foods. As I add recipes, I list the ingredients in the proper section. This helps make my time in the grocery store more efficient. I'm not backtracking through aisles. Learn your grocery store's layout and begin writing your lists in order.

Helpful Meal Planning Resources

If you really do not like the idea of meal planning, there are online services that will do it for you. These are usually reasonably priced. They will provide you with a list of meals for the week and a corresponding shopping list. Some of them will let you swap out meals and customize the plan to meet your tastes. Others do not. Many of them offer special plans, like gluten free. Some of them are geared toward a particular store. I listed some of my favorites on my website at *homeandfaith.com/resources*.

There are also online services that make meal planning easier for you, but you can still choose all your meals. I have used a service called Plan to Eat for several years, and I love it. I can import recipes that I find online with the click of a button. I can also type in recipes from cookbooks. I usually just add the ingredient list, the title of the cookbook, and the page of the recipe. Once I'm ready to prepare that meal, I know where to go to get the directions. Having all of my favorite recipes in one place makes it a lot easier when I am trying to add meals to my current meal plan. It is also helpful to be able to save new recipes that I want to try so I don't forget about them.

The service also has a built-in calendar. You can drag meals into the calendar and place them in breakfast, lunch, dinner, or snack slots for the appropriate day. Once you add a meal to the calendar, the ingredients are automatically added to a shopping list. I can connect to this shopping list to my phone to access at the store, or I can print it out. As I put the ingredients in my cart at the store, I check them off on my phone. It's very handy and makes meal planning even easier.

After Your Meal Plan Has Been Created

Once you've figured out which meals you plan to make, look them over to see if there are parts that need to be prepared ahead of time. For example, if we're going to have sandwiches during the next week, I need to make bread a day or so in advance. If I am going to cook beans from scratch, I need to soak them the day before. Make notes on your meal calendar for anything you'll need to do ahead of time and what day you'll do them on.

Some things don't necessarily have to be done ahead of time, but it may make your life a lot easier if you do. Take the time to wash and cut fruits and vegetables for the week. Go ahead and boil a pot of eggs if you will need hardboiled eggs during the week. These things are easy to do and will save you time when you're just trying to get food on the table as quickly as possible. This will make your meal prep faster and will also ensure the food actually gets eaten.

Another helpful habit to develop is to think ahead to the next meal while you are preparing the current meal. If you take a minute to think about what you'll be eating for dinner while you're making lunch, you can set out the needed ingredients or remember to thaw the meat. These little things can mean the difference between having a healthy meal for your family and going out to eat instead because you feel overwhelmed.

During dinner, think ahead to the following morning's breakfast. Most evenings, I try to prepare breakfast for the following morning. I can whip up a batch of muffins while dinner is cooking and then put them in the oven while we're eating. I always feel so relieved when I wake up in the morning knowing breakfast is ready. All I have to do is serve it. I know my children will have something healthy and filling to start their day, and I don't have to work up a sweat in the kitchen while I'm still groggy-eyed and half-asleep.

This schedule may not work for you. Find what does work. Play around with preparing foods at different times until you find your groove. The key here is to do a little thinking ahead. Just keep in mind what's coming up next and do the little things that are needed to make it smooth and easy. Use the time in your day when you're not as busy to get a head start so that you're ready to go when your day does get busy.

Now that you have a meal plan that's going to work for you, you must use it! If you make a meal plan and then forget to look at it, you'll be ordering delivery. Post it somewhere you will see it, like on the refrigerator. Add it to your planner if you use one. I find that putting it on the refrigerator is helpful because I'm not repeatedly answering the "What's for dinner?" question from my kids. They can look it up for themselves.

Find time in your day to review your upcoming meals. Review your plans in the evening for the next day or sit down with it in the morning. It doesn't matter when you do it, just ensure you make the time at some point in the day. The time you spent planning meals and shopping for them will be wasted if you don't actually take the time to review your plan. If you are not used to meal planning, this may actually be the hardest part!

The easiest way to form a new habit is to attach it to something you already do every day. If you normally sit down and make a to-do list in the morning, add checking your meal plan to this time. Or you can do it when you sit down to eat breakfast. Find an activity you do every day and anchor this new habit to it. Before long, it will be engrained and you won't have to think about it.

Be Flexible

The key to having a meal plan is to remember that the meal plan is there to work for you, not the other way around. If your plans change after making your meal plan, don't hesitate to switch meals to a different day. And don't beat yourself up if you can't make it work for a night and you need to go out to eat or order takeout. It's not the end of the world. Sometimes life gets busy and we need to do what we need to do to survive and get through. If you find this is happening often and you don't like it, then it's probably time to sit down and think about your priorities and decide what your goals are. If you want to serve your family healthy meals, it will take some time. You may need to re-evaluate your schedule.

Make Meals Ahead

Freezer meals are extremely helpful on busy evenings. These can be incorporated into your meal plan on both sides—when you make them and when you eat them. There are different ways to make freezer meals. Many people plan a weekend, or another day when they have plenty of time, and make ten or more meals at once. This can be an efficient way to cook. Set everything up assembly-line style and add ingredients to bags or other containers to prepare to freeze them.

It can also be money-saving, because you can split the same ingredients over several meals, leaving very little leftover ingredients that may potentially go to waste. However, it does take an investment up front, in both time and money. Because you are purchasing enough food to make ten or more meals for your freezer, plus the other meals you're planning for that week, it can be hard on your budget. Of course, you make that back in later weeks when you're not buying a meal because you're eating the food you froze. It also takes a sizable time investment. Cooking this way takes at least an afternoon, if not more.

I rarely have that amount of time in one solid chunk, so I prefer to do my freezer cooking a different way. I often plan one meal each week that freezes well and then I double it. I double the ingredients and add them to my shopping list. I also note on my meal plan that I need to make two on the night I'm serving that one. When it comes time to cook those meals, I just double everything and divide it between the two pans, or put half in a bag if that's how I'm going to freeze it. It takes very little extra time and effort, and I fill my freezer little by little.

Keep an inventory of what's in your freezer and use it when you're planning meals for future weeks. Add the freezer meal to your meal plan for an evening after a crazy day. Just remember to make a note in your prep section to pull the meal out of the freezer and put it in your refrigerator the night before so it's thawed and ready to cook the next day. You will thank yourself on those busy days when you have a meal ready and waiting to be heated up for dinner. For more in-depth details about freezer cooking and some wonderful resources to help you, please visit my website at *homeandfaith.com/resources.*

Chapter 5
How Do I Get Started?

Now we'll discuss a few basic changes that you can make so you'll be well on your way to cooking healthier meals for your family.

As I have previously stated, the key to making lasting changes in your kitchen—and subsequently your health—is to take it slow, one step at a time. Do not start with the hardest or most involved step. Pick something that excites you and that you think you can start right away. The changes introduced in this book will be broken down into baby steps. Some of them you may already be doing. Just pick up where you are and move forward from there. Sometimes, you may feel like you can skip over a few steps and move a little faster. That's fine, too.

Begin by evaluating your current ways of feeding your family. Are you eating out most nights? This is a good place to start. Pick one night and start making dinner at home. After you feel like you've got that under control, add another night. Continue doing this until you are eating at home most nights. If you are just starting to cook for your family, do not stress about making all your foods from scratch. Start with whatever you know how to cook. If it comes from a box or a can, that's still better than what you would get from a fast food restaurant.

This helps you get used to planning time to prepare food and for your family to get used to sitting around the dining table for meals. Once you're eating at home most nights, start to move on to better foods—making more from scratch and using less processed foods. Don't worry. It sounds like it will be hard and you will need hours in the kitchen. It won't be hard. I rarely spend more than thirty or forty-five minutes at a time cooking in my kitchen. This is where those kitchen "helpers" we talked about in chapter two come in handy.

You can look at this stage as a progression from eating out at restaurants, to preparing and serving meals that contain more processed, ready to go foods, to finally, cooking most of your food from scratch. Some restaurants do serve healthy food, and most at least have something that's somewhat healthy on their menus. I love to eat at restaurants. I'm not trying to say that your goal should be to never eat out. However, when you cook in your own kitchen, you have control over the ingredients. It becomes more affordable to eat healthier, too.

In the next section, I will discuss areas in which you can make changes, and we'll talk about how to make baby steps in those areas. There's no right order to follow. You can progress in one area for a while and then move to a different area, coming back to the first at a later time. However you choose to do it is fine. Finally, don't move too fast. Move at a speed that you are comfortable with. This is not a race. If you try too many new things at once, you will feel overwhelmed.

If you're learning a new way to cook or a new skill in the kitchen, don't add anything else new on top of it. Work at that skill until you can do it well and don't feel intimidated by it. Once this skill has become a habit, then move on to something else.

Above all, do not allow yourself to feel like a failure after a mistake or because you're not progressing as fast as you'd like. Give yourself grace! Some things will take practice. Learn from your mistakes so you can improve upon them next time. Whether it's making rice without burning it, or making a fresh batch of homemade whole wheat bread, you will eventually learn how to do it if you keep practicing and don't give up.

Making any progress toward healthier eating is better than not doing anything at all. So, while it may feel as if you're sometimes moving at a snail's pace, just know that any changes you make are benefitting you and your family. Something is better than nothing. If you try to do too much too quickly, you will feel overwhelmed and this may lead to quitting altogether.

Now let's get ready for the fun part! In the next section, we'll dive into ways that you can slowly transform your cooking. Let's get started!

Part Two

Chapter 6
Wheat and Other Grains

The order in which you make changes, and how quickly you progress, is entirely up to you and will be different for each person. If your progress is slower than you had hoped, don't let that frustrate you. It is much better to move slow and steady but make lasting changes than it is to speed through and not be able to maintain the changes. Just pick one area to work on and get started.

In my own kitchen, the first thing I changed was related to grains. It made such a huge impact on our lives and health that it is the main reason we continued to change other areas of our lives, too.

I resisted learning about these changes for a long time because I thought it would be hard to change and would take so much time that I would never be able to leave the kitchen. At the time, my oldest son was having a lot of problems digesting many types of food and was drinking most of his meals from a prescription formula. We had been told by his doctors that it would take quite a while for his digestive tract to heal, but we hoped that once it did, he would be able to eat real food, digest properly, and grow.

After about four years on the formula, he began to express an interest in eating what we were eating. This was huge because prior to being put on this formula, his relationship with food was not good. Most of what he ate left him in pain. He reacted almost with fear if he was presented with a new food. So, when he started asking to try foods that the rest of the family was eating, we definitely took notice. Around this time, I attended a conference for homeschooling families. During the weekend-long conference, there were many workshops from which the attendees could choose. During one of the workshop slots, there were no sessions that I was really interested in attending. So, I chose one about bread because I enjoyed cooking and was just becoming interested in new ways of cooking.

This workshop completely changed the way I thought about food. It knocked out all of my wrongly held beliefs that healthy cooking was too time consuming. After tasting samples that the workshop presenter had prepared, it convinced me that healthy food could taste really, really good! I knew we had to make changes. If my son and his fragile digestive system would begin experimenting with eating food again, I knew I had to do it right. If we allowed him to eat and it caused damage to his body again, I knew we would be so much worse off than we were the first time around. I am so thankful God led me to that specific workshop on that day. What I thought would be a time killer ended up changing our lives, and I haven't stopped talking about it since.

So, what did I learn in that workshop? I learned about flour. I learned that the flour sold in bags on the grocery store shelves has been stripped and depleted of its life-giving nutrients. It has been processed to the point that it can make us sicker by eating it. It is refined and packaged so that it can sit on shelves and not go bad. But it isn't healthy. Even the whole wheat flour on the shelves has lost most of its vital nutrients, has an awful texture, and just doesn't taste good. I fully believe that many of the problems people are having today with gluten is not the gluten itself, but the type of flour that the gluten is found in. Remember, though, I am not a doctor. If you have been advised to refrain from gluten because you have been diagnosed with celiac disease or some other allergy, please do not make changes in your diet without the supervision of your doctor.

Wheat Flour

Wheat flour from the store has been ground from wheat berries and then sifted out to remove the bran and germ from the flour. What is left is the endosperm. The bran contains the fiber from the wheat berry and the germ contains the vital nutrients. The germ will turn rancid quickly once the berry has been ground and the inside has been exposed to the air. This will not sell well. Nobody wants to buy rancid-tasting flour. So, to solve this, the germ is removed.

Once this process began in the 1920s, there was an increase in some diseases that previously had been very rare. Beriberi and pellagra became a problem again. It was determined that the cause of these diseases was due to a lack of B vitamins. You guessed it: these very vitamins, along with many others, are found in the germ of the wheat berry. So, what did flour manufacturers do? Rather than returning to freshly ground wheat flour, they made a synthetic version of some of these vitamins, ones that would be shelf-stable, and added them back into the sifted endosperm that makes our white flour.

This did solve the problem of the rising incidents of beriberi and pellagra, but our bodies will never be able to synthesize and utilize synthetic versions of vitamins the same way as natural vitamins. We can try to replicate what God has created, and many times we'll get close, but we'll never be able to make an exact copy.

Our bodies crave the food that God has made and provided for us. Chemicals from a laboratory will not be an adequate substitute in the long-term. This is why I believe we're seeing so many cases of gluten intolerance cropping up. I believe it is because we're not providing our bodies with the necessary nutrients alongside the gluten so that it can be digested properly. The whole wheat berry contains all of these nutrients. God knew what He was doing when He created our food.

Other Grains

There are grains other than wheat. We will return to wheat later on and discuss our options for better wheat flours, as well. We will also go into more detail about the practical steps that you can take to improve the wheat flour you use in your kitchen. For now, however, I'm going to touch on some of the other grains. Many of these are getting used more frequently now that people are becoming more conscious of the problems with wheat.

Some other common grains are oats, rice, barley, and quinoa. These can all be found in most grocery stores and are all naturally gluten free. If you have celiac disease, however, you will still want to purchase oats labeled as gluten free, as there can be cross contamination with small amounts of gluten otherwise. These are hearty and filling grains and can be added to your diet for variation. Oats are especially versatile and can be used to make traditional oatmeal as well as cookies, cakes, pancakes, and many other foods. It's a great way to add more carbohydrates to our diets and give us more energy. This is one reason oats are often found in breakfast foods. They offer a burst of energy to help get the day started.

Spelt is another grain that can be used in baking. It is similar to wheat. It has a sweet flavor and works well with muffins, cakes, cookies, and other sweet breads. It works well in quick breads and in yeast breads. When substituting spelt for whole wheat in recipes, you will generally need to add a little more spelt. Usually, one fourth cup of additional spelt is needed for each cup of wheat flour the recipe calls for. Spelt also takes less kneading time that wheat flour.

Incorporating Whole Wheat into Your Cooking

Wheat is probably the most common grain used and eaten in the United States. There are different types of wheat and different types of wheat flours. We will be delving more deeply into this.

As we have already discussed, all-purpose wheat flour found in the bags in the grocery store has been ground, sifted, and then synthetic vitamins have been added to it to replace those that have been sifted out. This is the most common type of flour used in home kitchens and it is the grain used in most pre-made baked goods that can be purchased. It is empty of nutrition, but because it's a carbohydrate, it is broken down into glucose, just like all other carbs. It is digested quickly because the fiber and other vital nutrients have been removed. It can spike your blood sugar and then cause it to crash quickly. This is why a diet full of refined, white flour can leave you feeling sluggish and depleted of energy. However, many people eat it and are used to its texture and flavor.

Switching to whole wheat flour may be difficult. Don't worry; I completely understand and have been there. However, I will show you how this can be done without sacrificing texture or flavor and by adding only a couple of minutes of extra time than you would spend baking with white flour.

The main types of wheat used to bake with are hard red wheat, hard white wheat, and soft white wheat. Hard red is a heartier wheat. It tastes nuttier and has a stronger flavor. Hard white wheat has a very mild flavor. Soft white wheat also has a mild flavor. These are all different types of wheat plants.

The wheat berries from the plant are ground into flour. When the whole berry is used and the flour is not sifted apart, the flour is whole wheat. This whole wheat flour begins to oxidize once the berry is open and exposed to oxygen, just like an apple or banana begins to oxidize and turn brown once it has been cut open. It doesn't take long before the flour has completely oxidized, lost much of its nutrient power, and the oils have become rancid. Therefore, the healthiest, most nutritious flour is that which has been ground just prior to using it for cooking. This is where a grain mill comes in.

For around $200 to $250 you can purchase a countertop electric grain mill. You just measure out the wheat berries and dump them into the top. Seconds later, the attached bucket will contain freshly milled flour that you measure just like you would measure flour from a store-bought bag. It's that simple!

Deciding which types of berries to use for different types of baked goods is not difficult, either. It basically comes down to whether you are making a baked good with yeast—like a loaf of sandwich bread or a pastry—or something that doesn't use yeast, like cookies, cakes, or quick breads. The other factor is your taste preference. For yeast breads, you use a hard wheat. You can use either hard red or hard white, or a combination of the two.

My family doesn't enjoy the stronger wheat taste that comes with hard red wheat, so we almost exclusively use hard white wheat for sandwich breads, rolls, and buns. If you are making a pastry or non-yeast bread, you would use soft wheat. That's it! That's all you need to know when deciding between these three most common wheats.

And the taste? It absolutely cannot be matched. Let go of all preconceived notions you may have about the taste of whole wheat bread. Most of it is made with ground hard red wheat that has been sifted and had vitamins and bran added back in. It is already rancid before the bread was even made. The texture is grainy and it just doesn't taste good. Bread made with freshly ground wheat, even hard red wheat, is not comparable. It is soft and delicious. Until you have tried it, please do not assume that you don't like whole wheat bread made with freshly ground flour.

I realize that most people do not already have a grain mill sitting on their counter just waiting to grind berries into nutritious whole wheat flour. For most of us, $200 to $250 isn't pocket change. What do you do if you don't have a grain mill? There are steps you can take to make your baked goods more nutritious. In the meantime, I strongly urge you to make a savings plan to save for a grain mill. You absolutely will not regret it and the impact it will have on your health will be enormous.

Baby Steps to Improving Baked Goods with Wheat in Your Kitchen

1. To begin making changes with wheat in your home, first take a minute to think about the bread products you currently consume and prepare for your family. Are they pre-made, store bought breads? Are they made from a box at home? Are they made with white flour or whole wheat flour? Are they made from scratch? What you're currently buying and eating will determine your starting point for making changes in your kitchen. There is no wrong starting point. Your ultimate goal is to get to the place where you are able to grind your own fresh flour and make your own breads and baked goods. Remember, there's no rush. This may take years, and that's okay. Some people will decide they'll never get to that point. Each family is different and has their own priorities. When you feel like you're doing all you can with your time and finances, and you feel good about your kitchen, then that's where you stop. Perhaps in the future, you will return to this and make more changes. Don't forget to give yourself grace. Don't compare what you are doing with what others are doing. Do your best, pray about what God would have you make as your priorities, and let the rest go. Make your expectations for yourself only what God has asked of you. Your worth is not tied up in how much you do in the kitchen.

2. If you normally buy white sandwich bread, the first step you can take is purchasing a healthier loaf. Read labels. Find one that is made with whole wheat flour. A label that says "100 percent wheat" is most likely not *whole* wheat. Unless it says "whole wheat," then it probably isn't. Often, manufacturers will just add coloring to give the bread that classic caramel color that whole wheat has, but they'll continue using white all-purpose flour. Try different brands until you find one your family likes. It may not be 100 percent whole wheat at first. It may contain a mix of all-purpose flour and whole wheat flour. It may also contain other whole grains. Just find a healthier bread that you will actually eat. There

are specialty bakeries in many larger cities that prepare very healthy, very tasty breads, often with freshly ground flour. These would be an excellent choice if you are able to purchase them.

3. The next step is to change the flour you buy. Even if you've never made homemade bread from scratch, you probably buy flour from the store for other baked goods on occasion. Simply switch the typical all-purpose flour to a whole white wheat flour. The keywords here are "whole" and "white." If you buy regular whole wheat flour from the grocery store, you will have the flour that leaves you with a dense, gritty product. If you have a hard time finding whole white wheat flour in your grocery store, many online stores carry it. If your family has sensitive palates and notices this switch, feel free to use half all-purpose and half whole white wheat flour. After a while, begin to lower the ratio by using one fourth all-purpose and three fourths whole white wheat. Then move on to *all* whole white wheat. This most likely won't be necessary. This technique is useful any time you are making changes and presenting your family with something new. I have found that kids especially have a hard time making changes to their favorite foods. Doing it slowly and gradually can make that transition unnoticeable and you will have their cooperation. If you and your family are more adventurous eaters, you won't have to do this, or you could do it more quickly.

4. The next step is to begin making some of your bread products from scratch. If you have made it to this step, then you've already replaced your all-purpose flour with a healthier, whole white wheat flour for your everyday cooking. Now you get to use it to make breads. Pick one thing that you would like to make this week and add it to your meal plan. This could be a breakfast item, a side item, whatever you would like. Once you feel good about that, increase to two items in a week.

Many people are scared by the thought of making bread at home, but you shouldn't be! It really isn't difficult. It doesn't take much of your time. At least, it doesn't take much of your focused, hands-on time. Some breads may take longer to fully complete, but much of this time is rising and baking that doesn't require anything from you. And if you have a bread machine, this task will be even easier.

The easiest bread products to make are non-yeast breads, so that's where we'll start. These include drop biscuits, muffins, and quick breads, among others, which do not require rising time. Just mix the ingredients as directed in the recipe and pour into the appropriate pan, or drop it onto a cookie sheet and then bake. Drop biscuits are quick and can be made while you're making the rest of your dinner.

Quick breads usually take a little longer to bake. I often make these while I'm making dinner and save them for breakfast the next day. I do the same with muffins. There are quite a few delicious breakfast foods you can make quickly in the evening, or at least begin to prepare, and have them ready for your family in the morning. You can put together the dry ingredients for pancakes and waffles the night before and store them in the refrigerator or freezer until the next morning. Keeping them cool will help to slow the oxidation process since you won't be making them right away.

In the morning, all you'll need to do is add the wet ingredients and cook them. At the end of this chapter, you will find a few recipes to get you started. These are recipes that I use regularly, and they're easy. For more recipes and great cookbooks, please visit my website at *homeandfaith.com*.

5. After you have mastered non-yeast breads, you'll be ready to delve into the world of yeast breads. You will love making your own bread. Your house will smell wonderful and the taste just doesn't compare to breads you've probably been buying from the store. If you have the budget for a grain mill and you're not ready to start making yeast breads, go ahead and skip to step six. You can use freshly ground flour for all other items and come back to this step when you're ready.

Baking sandwich bread does take longer than non-yeast breads, but as I've already mentioned, the time is mostly hands-off. I almost always make my sandwich bread by starting with a bread machine. I put my ingredients in the bread machine and set it on the dough setting. If you don't have a bread machine at this point, there are instructions for making bread without one in the recipe for basic bread dough at the end of this chapter. It will take more hands-on time than using a bread machine, but it's so worth it. Once you've tasted it, you're going to want to keep making it! Save up for a bread machine to make this task easier. That way, you're more likely to make it on a regular basis.

Each bread machine is different, so you'll want to double check the order that you should add ingredients. All the bread machines I've used required that the liquid ingredients be added first, followed by dry ingredients, ending with the yeast on top. You'll want to make sure you use warm water if your bread machine doesn't have a function that brings the ingredients to the perfect temperature. Yeast must have warmth in order to activate it. Too hot, however, will kill the yeast. You are looking for a temperature between 105 degrees and 110 degrees. This will feel like warm, not hot, bath water, or like the temperature of a heated baby bottle. This is very important. If all of your ingredients are cold, you will not have a nice loaf of bread. The dough will not rise. This is the same if the ingredients are too hot.

Another thing to check on your bread machine is that it includes rising time on the dough setting and doesn't just mix and knead the dough. If it does not include rising time, simply remove the mixed and kneaded dough to another bowl, cover it loosely with plastic wrap and let it sit for thirty minutes to an hour until it has doubled in size. It will look "poofy." I usually lightly spray the plastic wrap with oil so that the dough doesn't stick to it if it rises to the top of the bowl.

Once the dough has risen, it is time to shape it. Whether it's still in the bread machine pan or in another bowl, gently punch down the top of the dough to flatten it. That may seem like such a waste since you just waited for it to rise! Giving bread multiple rising times allows the gluten to develop further and makes for a softer, more pleasing texture in the finished bread loaf. I use a pastry mat on my counter and I sprinkle it with a liberal amount of flour. The dough will be a lot easier to work with if it is well-floured. If not, it can stick to the counter or pastry mat. You can do this directly on a clean counter if you do not have a pastry mat.

Once the dough is on the mat, I use a bench scraper to cut it into the number of pieces that I need. This will depend on what I am making. If I am making sandwich bread, I usually divide the dough in half to make two loaves of bread. For dinner rolls, I'll make thirty-two small lumps of dough. For hamburger buns, I'll use sixteen pieces. I can make smaller sandwich rolls with twenty pieces. You can decide how you want to divide up the dough based on what you are making. The smaller the piece of dough, the smaller the finished product.

To divide dough into a lot of smaller pieces, I begin with cutting the dough in half. Then I take one of those halves, and cut it in half. I continue doing this until I have the right number of pieces. So, for example, to make thirty-two dinner rolls, I'll divide the dough in half. Each half will give me sixteen pieces. Divide each of these in half again. These pieces will each make eight rolls.

Continue dividing each piece in half in this pattern until you have the total number of dough pieces that you'll need. I use the same dough recipe to make all of these different types of bread. Easy! You can, of course, mix and match what you're making, too. I often make one loaf of bread and use the other half for rolls or buns.

Once you have your dough divided, you'll need to shape it. For loaves of bread, just take your dough piece and loosely shape it into a log the length of your pan. This doesn't have to look pretty. It will rise again and most irregularities will even out. Just make sure the log is fairly even. You don't want one end to be really skinny or flat. Plop it into your pan and you're ready to let it rise for the second time.

For rolls and buns, just take your small lumps of dough and pull the edges down to the bottom. The goal is to make a ball shape with the edges all coming together on the bottom. Pinch the edges together on the bottom as best you can. Once these rise and bake, you will not see any of this, even if you do look at the bottom. The top should be nice and smooth and round.

Once your rolls or buns are shaped, put them bottom-side down on a pan. If you place them fairly close together, they will rise up as they expand. If you spread them farther apart, they will be wider, and less tall. This is up to you and the intended use of the bread. For instance, you will probably want your hamburger buns to be wider and shorter and dinner rolls to be taller. They will all taste good, though!

Once you have shaped your dough, you need to let it rise once more. For bread, I let it rise until it's just starting to come up over the top of the pan. For buns and rolls, I let them rise until they are about double in size. The warmer your house is, the faster the dough will rise. I usually set mine on top of the stove. I don't always cover mine, but if you are concerned that it might dry out, then feel free to cover the dough with a damp tea towel. Preheat the oven to the temperature in the recipe and bake the bread as directed.

Once done, it should be golden brown on top and sound hollow when you tap on it. If you want to be sure that it's done, you can insert a thermometer probe through the corner toward the middle of the loaf. If should be about 190 degrees. Let it sit in its pan for about ten minutes, then remove it and let it sit on a wire cooling rack before slicing. I use a serrated bread knife to slice my bread. It cuts right through without tearing it.

6. If you have made it through all the previous steps, then you are doing wonderfully! You should feel very proud of your accomplishments; you've begun providing your family with freshly made baked goods. The only step left is to purchase your grain mill and grains. This is very easy! For recommendations on grain mills and sources for grains, please visit my website at *homeandfaith.com/resources*.

Once you have your mill and grains, all you need to do is choose which grain you need for your recipe and grind the grain. On average, one cup of wheat berries produces about one and a half cups of flour. This is not exact. I will use this for an idea of how many cups of berries I should grind. I measure those and put them in my mill and then I measure the exact amount of flour for my recipe once it has been ground. Use this freshly ground flour just like you would any other flour. If the recipe calls for one cup of white flour, simply use one cup of freshly ground flour.

Sometimes, after you have added the right amount of flour, the batter or dough may seem too wet. It can take freshly ground flour longer to soak up liquids than store-bought flour. If the dough is too wet, let it rest for five to ten minutes. This will almost always take care of this problem. If it is still too wet, add flour a little at a time until it is the right consistency. For bread dough, you want it to be slightly tacky. If it is too dry, your bread will be dry as well. And, to review, use soft white wheat in non-yeast breads and pastries, and hard white or hard red wheat in yeast breads.

I keep freezer bags in my freezer labeled with the different types of flours that I use. If I have any flour leftover in my canister after I've gotten what I need for the recipe, then I add it to the bag. Keeping the flour in the freezer will slow down the oxidation. I use this leftover flour for sprinkling on my counter or pastry mat when rolling out or kneading dough. I'll also use this when I only need a couple of tablespoons of flour for something, like when making gravy. I'll even use larger amounts in recipes if I find that my bag is getting full. It's probably not as nutritious as freshly ground flour, but I'd rather use it than let it go to waste.

These same steps can be followed for the other grains you'd like to use in your kitchen. Start by changing the items you're currently buying in the store. Buy the healthiest item you can find and afford. Slowly begin buying these other flours to use in your kitchen. You can grind many of them yourself if you have a grain mill. You can grind corn or popcorn in your mill to make cornmeal. You can grind beans of various types to make bean flours. You can also grind white or brown rice to make rice flour.

To make oat flour, just put rolled oats into a food processor or blender and process them until you have flour. While technically not a grain, you can also do this with almonds to make almond flour. Just be sure to turn the processor off when you have flour. If you over-process, you will end up with almond butter—which isn't necessarily bad, just not what you're trying for here.

Many grains can be eaten in ways other than grinding them for flours. Popcorn kernels can be popped in a small amount of oil and salted for an easy, healthy snack. Oats can be used to make oatmeal for a quick breakfast. They can also be added to many baked goods and can be used to make delicious, easy granola. I have included one of our favorite granola recipes at the end of this chapter. You don't want to miss this: one of our favorite breakfasts served with milk or on top of yogurt.

Barley, quinoa, and even wheat berries can be cooked and used in salads and other side dishes. Rice can be made and eaten with dinner. Leftovers can be used to make rice pudding. There are so many different grains and different ways to serve them. Please do not eliminate all grains from your diet. They are an essential part of health. And, unless you have a true allergy or intolerance to wheat or gluten, don't leave this healthy whole grain out of your kitchen!

There will be times in your life when you have progressed through multiple steps and then you may find yourself unable to keep up with these changes because of time, health, or financial reasons. Be willing to give yourself permission to step back down to a place that is more manageable. Once you are able, work your way back to where you want to be. Follow this advice in all of the areas of your kitchen—and life—and you will eliminate the stress that comes with placing unrealistic expectations on yourself.

Take it slowly and make changes as you're ready. Enjoy your journey, work hard, and give yourself all the grace you need. You will reap the benefits!

Basic Bread Dough

This basic bread dough recipe can be used to make sandwich bread, hamburger buns, and dinner rolls. It can be made in the bread machine or by hand. It is so versatile and very easy. Try it!

1 ½ cups hot water

1/3 cup oil

1/3 cup honey

2 teaspoon salt

1 egg

1 tsp. gluten

4 ½ to 5 ½ cups freshly ground flour (hard white, hard red, or a combination of both)

1 tablespoon yeast

To make by hand:

1. Combine water, oil, honey, salt, and egg in a large bowl. Add the gluten and 2 ½ cups of the flour. Mix thoroughly. Add the yeast and enough flour to form a soft dough. The dough will be only slightly sticky, but able to be worked with.

2. Knead the dough until it is smooth and elastic. This will take about five or six minutes. (If you want to double this batch, the kneading time will increase to about eight minutes. If you triple the recipe, increase kneading time to about 12 minutes.)
3. Return the dough to the bowl and cover with a tea towel. Set it in a warm place and let it rise until it has doubled in size. This will take about an hour.

4. After it has doubled, shape it into the desired shape. This amount of dough will make two loaves to be put into greased loaf pans. (I like silicone-coated loaf pans. No greasing required!) It will be enough for 16 hamburger buns, or 32 dinner rolls. I place the rolls or buns on a greased baking sheet or lined with a silicone baking sheet.

5. Set the pans in a warm place and let the dough rise again until doubled. I find that this second rise is usually shorter (about thirty minutes) and I don't cover them. If it is taking longer and you are finding that the dough is drying out, you can lay a damp towel on the dough. I preheat my oven after the dough has been rising for about twenty or twenty-five minutes. I set the pans on the top of my stove for the last ten minutes or so, while the oven is preheating. This extra warmth helps the bread rise more quickly.

For loaves of bread: Preheat the oven to 350 degrees and bake for twenty-five to thirty minutes. The bread will look golden brown on top, sound hollow when tapped, and should be about 190 degrees if you insert a thermometer into it.

For buns or dinner rolls: Preheat the oven to 400 degrees and bake for eight to 10 minutes, until golden brown.

If I make one loaf of bread and use the other half for eight buns or 16 rolls, I bake them all together in a 350-degree oven. I pull the buns or rolls out after about 12 to 15 minutes and let the bread continue baking for 10 to 15 minutes more.

To make dough using a bread machine:

1. Add the ingredients to the pan of your bread machine in the order listed by your bread machine manufacturer. This is usually, but not always, liquids first followed by dry ingredients. I put my

liquids in the bottom with the salt and gluten. I add all of the flour and end with the yeast on the top.

2. Set the machine to the dough setting. If your machine does not have a rise time included in the dough setting, then remove the dough to a large bowl and continue with step three (above) after the dough has been mixed and kneaded.

3. If your machine does include rising time, continue with step four (above) after the cycle has completed.

Recipe adapted with permission from The Bread Beckers. For the original recipe, please visit www.breadbeckers.com/blog/basic-dough-recipe/

Easy Chocolate Cinnamon Granola

This is such an easy breakfast! My kids love it. Make it the evening before and you will have a nutritious, filling breakfast waiting for your family the next morning.

3 cups old-fashioned or rolled oats

2 cups quick oats

1 cup coconut sugar or brown sugar

1 cup flaked or shredded unsweetened coconut

2 teaspoons cinnamon

1 teaspoon nutmeg (I find grated fresh nutmeg tastes so much better than dried nutmeg. You can find fresh nutmeg in your spice aisle. They look like round nuts. Use a microplane held above your bowl to grate the nutmeg right into your other ingredients. If I don't have fresh nutmeg, I leave it out altogether.)

½ cup of water

½ cup unrefined coconut oil, melted (You can use olive or avocado oil, but the coconut oil adds a wonderful flavor.)

1 tablespoon vanilla extract

1 cup chocolate chips

Preheat the oven to 325 degrees F.

1. Mix both kinds of oats, coconut sugar, coconut, cinnamon, and nutmeg together in a large bowl.

2. Add water, oil, and vanilla extract to the oat mixture and mix thoroughly.

3. Divide between two 9- by 13-inch casserole pans.

4. Put both pans in the oven for 15 minutes. Stir and put back in the oven for 15 more minutes. Stir again. I begin checking whether it's done at this point. If the granola is not golden brown and beginning to crisp, add five more minutes of cooking time.

5. After it is golden brown, add ½ cup of chocolate chips to each pan and mix thoroughly.

6. Turn the oven off and put the pans back in the oven. Allow them to sit in the oven for at least two hours, or overnight. This allows the granola to continue to dry and crisp without overcooking it.

7. Serve with milk, like cereal, or as a topping for yogurt.

Easy and Delicious Pumpkin Bread

I love pumpkin year round, but especially in the fall. This bread makes a good breakfast or a snack later in the day.

2 cups flour (I use freshly milled soft white wheat)

1 cup coconut sugar or other granulated sweetener

1/4 teaspoon baking powder

3/4 teaspoon salt

1 teaspoon baking soda

1/2 teaspoon cinnamon

1/2 teaspoon cloves

1/2 teaspoon nutmeg

2 eggs, lightly beaten

1/2 cup melted coconut oil, avocado, or olive oil

1/2 cup cold water

1 cup mashed pumpkin

1 teaspoon vanilla

1. Preheat the oven to 325 degrees F.

2. In a medium bowl, add the flour, sugar, and all of the spices. Whisk together until well-mixed.

3. Add the eggs, oil, water, pumpkin, and vanilla to the dry ingredients.

4. Mix with a spoon until the dry ingredients are just moistened. You don't want to over-mix the batter or the bread will turn out dry.

5. Spray the inside of a loaf pan with an oil spray.

6. Pour the batter into the pan and bake in the preheated oven for one hour and 10 minutes, or until a toothpick inserted into the center comes out clean.

Pizza Dough

Pizza dough is easy and fun to make. Why order delivery when you can make your own at a lower cost? It doesn't take long and it tastes so good! Give it a try on your next pizza night.

2 cups of warm water (105 to 115 degrees F)

2 tablespoons active dry yeast

2 teaspoons sugar

2 teaspoons salt

4 tablespoons oil (olive, avocado, or refined coconut oil, melted)

5 cups flour (I use hard white wheat)

1. Add the warm water to a large bowl and sprinkle the yeast on top. Stir to dissolve the yeast.

2. Add the remaining ingredients and mix them together with a spoon.

3. Turn the dough out onto a floured surface and knead the dough for two to five minutes until it is smooth and no longer sticky.

4. Divide the dough in half, roll each half and shape it on a baking stone or greased pizza pan.

5. Add pizza sauce (I have a great recipe here), cheese, and toppings of your choice.

6. Bake at 500 degrees for 10 minutes, or until the crust looks crispy and lightly browned.

This dough can be frozen for later use. Divide the dough in half and place each half in an airtight freezer bag. Freeze for up to four to six weeks. To use, place the frozen dough in a greased bowl and thaw at room temperature for at least three to four hours. Roll, shape and bake as directed above.

While this dough is quick and easy to make in the evening before dinner, I have also made it in my bread machine. I add the ingredients, set the machine to the dough setting, and then divide, shape, and bake as directed above. This is handy if I am going to be out of the house in the late afternoon and won't have much time to prepare dinner.

Recipe adapted with permission from The Money Saving Mom. For the original recipe, please visit www.moneysavingmom.com/2012/05/4-weeks-to-fill-your-freezer-freezer-friendly-pizza-dough-day-13.html.

Drop Biscuits

Drop Biscuits are so easy to make and a great place to start if you are new to making your own bread. They don't need any kneading or rising and come together so quickly.

2 cups flour (I use freshly ground soft white wheat)

1 teaspoon baking powder

2 teaspoons granulated sweetener

¼ teaspoon salt

½ cup melted butter

¾ cup milk

1. Preheat the oven to 450 degrees F.

2. Combine the flour, baking powder, sweetener, and salt in a large bowl. Stir in the melted butter and milk until the dry ingredients are moistened. Don't over-mix.

3. Drop the mixture using a tablespoon onto a cookie sheet that has been lightly greased or lined with a silicone baking mat.

4. Bake in the preheated oven for eight to 12 minutes until the edges are golden brown.

Baked Pancake

This is a quick way to serve pancakes for breakfast. On busy mornings, when you don't have time to flip pancakes on a griddle, try popping these into the oven instead. They are so good!

1 cup buttermilk or 1 cup of milk with a splash of apple cider vinegar

2 large eggs, lightly beaten

4 tablespoons coconut oil or butter, melted

2 tablespoons honey granules, evaporated cane juice, or other granulated sweetener

1/4 cup sour cream

2 tablespoons maple syrup, plus more for serving

2 cups flour (I use freshly milled soft white wheat)

4 teaspoons baking powder

½ teaspoon salt

1/2 cup mini chocolate chips

1. Preheat the oven to 350 degrees F.

2. Add the buttermilk (or milk and vinegar), eggs, and melted coconut oil to a medium bowl. Whisk it together. If you are using coconut oil instead of butter, you will need to whisk this together right away. Once the coconut oil hits the colder milk and eggs, it will begin to solidify.

3. Add the sweetener, sour cream, and maple syrup to the liquids.

4. In another bowl, whisk the flour, baking powder, and salt together. Stir in the chocolate chips.

5. Add the dry ingredients to the wet ingredients and mix just until the dry ingredients have been incorporated. A few small lumps are fine. Do not over-mix or the pancakes will be dry.

6. Pour this batter into a 9- by 13-inch glass or metal baking pan, sprayed with a cooking oil. (I love to use silicone coated pans. They are nonstick and everything comes right out of them.)

7. Bake the pancake for 18 to 20 minutes, or until it is lightly browned around the edges. Cut into squares and serve with extra maple syrup.

Chapter 7
Fresh Produce

Adding more fruits and vegetables to our diets is something that most of us could benefit from. Most people do not get nearly enough fruits and vegetables. These provide so many important nutrients and can be prepared in many different ways.

Fruits

Fruits are usually easier to eat enough of because they provide that natural sweetness that most of us enjoy. Buying fresh fruits and having them available to grab quickly helps us remember to eat them. Apples, bananas, oranges, and grapes are quick and easy snacks. Fun dips can be whipped together easily if you want to give your family something different every now and then. They can be packed in lunches or added as a side to dinner at home. They can also be blended and added to smoothies. Fresh berries are another easy option. It's best for your budget if you buy these in the summer months. Fresh strawberries, sliced or cut into chunks and served with homemade whipped cream make a wonderful dessert.

Vegetables

Fresh vegetables can also make a quick snack. Carrot or celery sticks are easy to package up and have ready to go. Bell peppers can be sliced to have on the side of a meal, as well. We really like to eat our fresh vegetables dipped in homemade ranch dressing. My kids think it is more fun to dip their veggies in something, and if you do not enjoy the taste of many vegetables, the ranch dressing makes them taste less bland. I have included the recipe for ranch dressing that we use. It is so good—try it!

Another way to get more raw vegetables into your diet is to make salads. It's so easy to chop or tear up a head of lettuce and slice a few tomatoes. That's usually all I do for the main part of my salads. Sometimes I will add spinach leaves to it, as well. If you don't have much time, a bag of pre-shredded salad mix will do the job, but honestly it doesn't take too much longer to just chop a head of lettuce. It's also easier on your wallet.

I use a serrated knife when I cut lettuce. It's easier to handle because it doesn't slip around as much on the lettuce. To chop a head of lettuce, turn it so that it's stem-side up. Cut it in half through the stem. Take that half and lay it cut-side down so that it's flat. Cut it in half again. Take one of those parts (one fourth of the head) and cut the stem out with a diagonal cut. Now, making sure that one of the cut sides is down so that this part of the head of lettuce is lying flat, cut it into slices. Cut them as thick as you would like them. Lay these slices flat and cut them the opposite way. This will make shorter strips. Repeat this with each quarter until you have enough for your family.

Place all these cut pieces into the basket of a salad spinner and rinse them under running water. Put the basket into the salad spinner and spin until the lettuce is dry and crisp. I often just pour out the water from the salad spinner and then dump the lettuce into the base and serve the salad right out of that. It's not fancy, but it works and it leaves me with less dishes to wash.

I toss in some chopped tomatoes, and I use a serrated knife to slice and chop them, as well. I buy bags of dried cranberries and sunflower seeds. I shred a block of cheese. We pass these around the table with the salad, and each person can add whichever toppings they would like. We sometimes add nuts, hard boiled eggs, or other vegetables, like avocado slices if I have them. We almost always have homemade ranch dressing and sometimes we have other dressings as well. This makes for a very easy, but very tasty salad. This is a great way to start almost any meal.

Other Ways to Incorporate Fresh Produce

When you are grocery shopping, don't overlook your freezer aisle when it comes to fruits and veggies. These are picked at their peak time for ripeness and immediately frozen. They have not had time to lose many nutrients, so they are a healthy alternative to fresh produce, especially when you're shopping for them outside of their growing season.

When you buy fresh produce during a time when it cannot be grown in the area in which you live, this means it was grown far away, often in another country. It was picked long before it was ripe. In this case, the ripening often finishes in the back of a truck. By the time it gets to the store, the produce is many miles away from where it was grown and it's been sitting in a truck for quite a while. The cost will be much higher than it would have been if it was grown closer to home in season.

Frozen fruits and vegetables can be thawed and added to recipes in the same way you would add fresh produce. Frozen veggies can be steamed or roasted directly from their frozen state. Add some butter and salt and you have an easy, healthy side dish. Frozen fruit can be thawed and added to yogurt, breads, or cobblers that call for fruit. You can also make smoothies with fruit straight from the freezer.

Canned fruits and vegetables are the least healthy option. The high heat used in canning kills many of the nutrients. Many times, a large amount of salt is added to help preserve vegetables. Fruits are often canned in syrupy liquid. While these are the least healthy options, I still believe they are better than nothing. Sometimes, single-serving fruit cups are all I have time for. If I want my children to have fruit with their lunch, this might be the best that I can do at the time. I try to have fresh fruit available as often as I can, but when I know we'll have a busy week and will be squeezing lunch in between various activities, then I will have these on hand. My kids can get them out of the pantry and open them by themselves.

The steps to improving your fruit and vegetable intake are simple.

1. Buy it! It doesn't matter which type you buy, just buy some. If you rarely eat fruits or vegetables now, I would suggest starting with fruits. Buy a bag of apples or a bunch of bananas. Pack one in lunch boxes or serve them at breakfast with a scoop of peanut butter as a dip. Add them into your diet as often as you can. Buy a bag of grapes, wash them, and use kitchen scissors to cut the stems apart into smaller pieces. Serve these with lunch or alongside dinner. Begin increasing your fruit intake one meal at a time.

2. Buy a bag of frozen vegetables and serve them with dinner. To steam frozen veggies, add a couple of inches to the bottom of a pot. Bring the water to a boil and place a steamer tray above the water. Pour in the amount that you want and put a lid on the pot. Allow the vegetables to steam for five to ten minutes. Check them after five minutes and see if they are cooked to your desired tenderness. If not, leave them in a little longer.

If you don't have a steamer tray, or if you just want a different taste, you can roast them on a cookie sheet in the oven. To do this, preheat the oven to 400 degrees. Place a silicone baking mat on the cookie sheet and pour in the frozen vegetables. They do not have to be thawed. Pour on a couple "glugs" of olive oil or refined coconut oil. This doesn't have to be precise. You just want enough to adequately coat the vegetables. Don't pour on too much. If you want to measure it out, I would use one to two tablespoons of oil for a pound of vegetables. Use a wooden or silicone spoon to stir the vegetables until they are all coated with the oil. Sprinkle on some salt. Again, this doesn't need to be measured precisely. Be liberal with the salt. Roast the vegetables for 30 to 45 minutes, stirring them around every 10 minutes. Once they are browned around the edges and can be easily poked with a fork, they are done. Experiment with different types and mixes of vegetables and find the ones your family likes the best. I really like roasted vegetables. The roasting seems to bring out the natural sugars, and they taste so good.

3. Try cooking fresh vegetables. I like to roast these the same way that I described above with the frozen vegetables. This is especially good in the fall with white potatoes and sweet potatoes added in. I don't even peel them. I just chop them into chunks that are about one inch cubes and spread them out on the tray. You can add sliced onion, mushrooms, broccoli, carrots, bell peppers, or anything else you want to try. Some vegetables, like root vegetables, take longer to cook. You may want to start these and then add in some of the more delicate vegetables later. I usually roast a pan of root vegetables for about 45 minute to one hour. If I am adding quicker cooking vegetables, I'll add them about fifteen to twenty minutes after I start the others. This is such a delicious way to serve vegetables!

4. Add raw vegetables to some of your meals. You can buy baby carrots in a bag, which are so easy to serve. Just open the bag, pour them in a bowl, and you're ready to go! You can slice a cucumber into circles. Bell peppers can be sliced into strips. To slice a bell pepper, cut the top and bottom off the pepper. Carefully run your knife around the inside edge to cut out the seeds. Pull the seeds out. You should now have the hollowed pepper. Turn it on its end so that it sits flat and slice it from top to bottom all the way around and you'll have spears of peppers to munch on. Try different colors! I don't find that the different colors taste much different from each other, but having a variety of colors keeps your plates interesting and adds a little more fun to the table. Remember to make some ranch dressing for dipping your fresh veggies!

Adding Variety

Try different types of fruits and vegetables and find the ones your family likes the best. Be adventurous and try things that may be completely new to you. A fruit that we tried for the first time this past year are kumquats. They look like tiny little oranges and they are eaten with the peel on. Just wash them and eat one. They reminded me of sour candy because they're sweet and sour at the same time and a little addicting. My family loved them. Take your children with you to the grocery store and let them pick out a fruit for snack or for sharing with the family. They will enjoy looking at the different fruits available, and they're often more likely to eat foods they helped pick out.

Some of our favorite fruits, besides the ones mentioned above, are kiwis and apricots. I cut the brown, fuzzy peel off the kiwi and slice the green fruit into circles. My kids eat them so fast! For apricots, plums, and peaches, though, I just wash them and they're ready to go. When my kids were small, I sliced them so they wouldn't have to worry about the pit. This didn't take much time and my children really enjoyed them.

Fruits and vegetables provide so many vitamins and other nutrients, as well as fiber. Include them in your diet as often as possible. Just increasing the amounts of fruits and veggies you are getting, if you don't currently eat much, will make a huge difference in your health and diet. Add butter and salt to vegetables. Try different cooking methods. Whip up some dips to add some variety and change up the tastes. Find easy, grab-and-go fruits and vegetables to pack into lunchboxes. Enjoy the bounty of these foods that God has given us in different seasons!

Easiest Smoothie Recipe

This recipe is quick to whip up in the morning and it can be customized with different fruits, yogurt flavors, and juice. My kids love this smoothie alongside some turkey bacon or eggs! This recipe will make two servings.

¾ to 1 cup orange juice

2 cups vanilla yogurt

1 – 1 ½ cups frozen strawberries

1. Add ¾ cup orange juice to the bottom of the blender container. Add yogurt. Add frozen strawberries on top.

2. Blend until well-mixed and no strawberry chunks remain.

3. If you would like your smoothie thinner, add more orange juice, a tablespoon at a time.

Ranch Dressing Mix

This is the *best* ranch dressing I've ever had! It is great as a dressing on a salad, but also wonderful as a dip for veggies. This mix will make multiple batches.

5 tablespoons dried minced onions

7 teaspoons parsley flakes

4 teaspoons salt

1 teaspoon garlic powder

1. Mix all of the dry ingredients in a jar or other container with a lid. Use this mix to make the dressing, as needed.

To make the dressing:

1 cup sour cream

½ cup milk

½ cup mayonnaise

1 tablespoon apple cider vinegar

2 tablespoons of ranch dressing mix

1. In a medium-sized mixing bowl, whisk together the sour cream, milk, mayonnaise, and vinegar until well-combined.

2. Add the ranch dressing mix and stir until thoroughly incorporated.

This can be used immediately, but it tastes better after the flavors have mingled for a couple of hours in the refrigerator.

Homemade Pressure Cooker Applesauce

You can make applesauce in an electric pressure cooker very quickly. It tastes so good and you can control the amount of sugar added. This recipe will make about two cups of applesauce.

8 apples (I like Gala apples, but you can use any kind you want. You can mix and match, too. Some apples are sweeter than others, so the types of apples you use will affect how much sweetener you need to add. I don't add much, if any, when I use Gala apples.)

¼ cup water

1 tablespoon lemon juice

1 teaspoon cinnamon (this can be omitted if you want plain applesauce)

Granulated sweetener, optional

1. Wash and peel the apples. Cut the apple off the core in four pieces. Place the apple pieces, water, and lemon juice in the pressure cooker pot.

2. Seal the pressure cooker and set it to cook on high pressure for three minutes.

3. After three minutes of cooking time, let the pressure cooker release its pressure naturally. Do not vent the pressure cooker.

4. Once the pressure has come down, open the lid and allow the apples to cool down for five to 10 minutes.

5. They will be very soft and you can mash them with the back of a spoon or a potato masher if you like chunky applesauce. Our family like smoother applesauce, so I use an immersion blender to blend the apples. You can also put the applesauce in a blender in small batches. Be careful—it's still hot!

6. Sample the applesauce to test for sweetness. If it's too tart for your taste, add sweetener one tablespoon at a time, stirring it in until it's to your liking. Add cinnamon, if desired.

Fruit Dip

Fruit slices are wonderful on their own, but every now and then it's fun to add a sweet dip. Little kids seem to eat more if they can dip their food into something!

12 ounces cream cheese, softened

¼ cup honey or maple syrup

2 teaspoons vanilla

½ teaspoon sea salt

2 tablespoons lemon juice

1 ½ cups whipping cream

Add all the ingredients except the whipping cream to a medium-sized mixing bowl or the bowl of a stand mixer and beat with a mixer for one to two minutes until well-combined and fluffy, scraping the sides of the bowl with a spatula, if necessary. Once combined, add the whipping cream and beat until stiff peaks form.

This will last in the refrigerator for about five days.

Recipe used with permission from Venison for Dinner. For the original recipe, please visit www.teamschat.wordpress.com/2017/02/02/fruit-dip/.

Homemade Whipped Cream

Homemade whipped cream is so easy to make and tastes *so good*. Whip up a batch to add to sliced strawberries or peaches.

1 cup heavy whipping cream

1 tablespoon granulated sweetener

Add ingredients to a medium-sized mixing bowl or the bowl of a stand mixer. Using the whisk attachment, whisk until soft peaks form.

Italian Dressing Mix

This makes a wonderful homemade Italian dressing mix. The mix can be used to make salad dressing or to flavor chicken or roasts. Use it just like you would a packet of Italian dressing mix that you might buy in the store. Use about two tablespoons of this mix to replace a packet.

2 tablespoons dried oregano

1 tablespoon onion powder

1 tablespoon granulated sweetener

1 tablespoon dried parsley

1 ½ teaspoon garlic powder

1 teaspoon dried basil

1 teaspoon black pepper

½ teaspoon salt

¼ teaspoon dried thyme

¼ teaspoon celery flakes

Mix all of the ingredients together in a jar or another container with a lid.

To make the dressing for salad or pasta salad:

2/3 cup avocado or olive oil

¼ cup vinegar—any kind that you like. Different kinds will give you different flavors. Try Balsamic, Red Wine, Apple Cider, or White Vinegar.

2 tablespoons water

2 tablespoons Italian dressing mix

Mix the oil, vinegar, and water with a whisk into a jar. Add the dressing mix and stir together. This can be used immediately, but it tastes better after the flavors have mingled for a few hours in the refrigerator. While this dressing sits, the oil and vinegar will separate. Simply shake the jar to mix before pouring onto salad.

Chapter 8
Sweeteners

Everyone enjoys a sweet treat from time to time, right? In my experience, if I try to eliminate all sugars and treats, I crave them more than any other food. It seems like whenever I can't have something for some reason, even if it's self-imposed, it becomes all I think about. When I eventually give in, it's not just a small taste of the forbidden food, it's a plateful.

I have learned over the years that trying to cut something completely out of my diet almost never works for me. I become obsessed with that specific food and have a hard time thinking about anything else. The last thing I want to do is obsess; it creates an unhealthy relationship with food. But, we all know that too much sugar is not healthy and can even be addictive. Is there a way to treat ourselves and still keep our diets healthy? Yes! The key is choosing healthier sweeteners and using them in moderation.

White and Brown Sugar

White sugar is probably the most familiar sugar. Today, in the United States, this sugar comes from sugar beets, as well as cane sugar. The sugar from these beets is extracted and separated from the rest of the plant. This raw sugar is then further refined to remove impurities and whiten the final product. This is also true of refined, white sugar that comes from sugar cane. The majority of sugar beets grown in the United States have been genetically modified.

Brown sugar commonly found in supermarkets is very similar. It is basically white sugar with molasses added to it. Molasses is a byproduct of the refining process of white sugar from sugar cane. Basically, molasses is removed from the sugar and then added back in after the sugar cane has been refined. Adding molasses to make brown sugar gives it the color, and it changes the taste. It adds a small amount of minerals, but it doesn't add enough benefits to make brown sugar any healthier than white sugar.

White sugar is a monosaccharide. It is digested very quickly, entering the bloodstream shortly after eating, and it raises your blood sugar. Insulin is then released to clean up and distribute the excess sugar, often doing its job overzealously, leaving you with a blood sugar crash and craving more. This can be a vicious cycle and can leave you feeling dependent on getting more and more sugar.

Other Common Sweeteners

There are other sweeteners available at most grocery stores. These include unrefined cane sugar, honey, maple syrup, coconut sugar, and stevia. Some other sweeteners available in health stores or online include natural cane sugar, such as Sucanat and honey granules.

Many of these are better options than white or brown sugar. Natural sugars contain nutrients that help your body digest them. While they do still contain sugar molecules, the extra nutrients help curb the vicious blood sugar cycle that white sugar can cause. This doesn't mean they can be consumed with abandon, though. They will still convert to fat if eaten in excess. Your body will use what it needs and store the rest in your fat cells. Fat cells can stretch as big as needed to store any excess. This is how our jean sizes can continue to increase.

Having a sweet treat in moderation is totally fine. It helps curb the cravings and brings us enjoyment. However, making a meal out of cake and ice cream on a regular basis, even if it's completely sweetened with honey, will not help. Do not deprive yourself of all sweet pleasures. Just consume them wisely.

Alternative Sweeteners

The sugars I use in my home most of the time are honey, maple syrup, honey granules, and coconut sugar. Occasionally, I will use unrefined cane sugar or brown sugar if I am looking for a certain appearance or taste in the dessert I am baking. We do not enjoy the flavor of sugars like Rapadura or Sucanat, so I use coconut sugar as a replacement for brown sugar when I need it.

You may find that you do like certain sugar flavors. Experiment with different types until you find the sugar your family likes the most. I use honey granules as a replacement for white sugar. It has a yellow tint and may leave your baked goods a little bit darker than white sugar, but the taste difference is negligible.

This is a very easy substitution. If a recipe calls for one cup of sugar, simply replace it with one cup of honey granules. The same can be said for trading brown sugar with coconut sugar. I am easily able to find coconut sugar in my local grocery stores. Check yours and see if they carry it. I order honey granules online. However, large health food stores may carry it. For specific recommendations, please visit *homeandfaith.com/resources*.

Steps for Using Healthier Sweeteners

1. The first step is to use up what you already have in your kitchen. Begin making some cookies or brownies from scratch. You may still be using white sugar, but you will know exactly what you are adding to your desserts. There will be no preservatives or unpronounceable ingredients. This alone is better than making premade cookies or even cookies from a mix.

2. Replace your white and brown sugars with a healthier granulated sugar that you can find in your local grocery store. This could be unrefined cane sugar, coconut sugar, or honey granules, if you can find them. Stevia is also readily available. Stevia is a dried sugar from the stevia plant. It is extremely sweet—much sweeter than sugar. Consequently, it takes a very tiny amount to achieve the desired sweetness. Using stevia in baked goods requires a learning curve. I do not enjoy the flavor of stevia and use it very rarely.

3. Experiment with liquid, natural sweeteners. Honey and maple syrup are excellent sweeteners. They will lend different flavors to your desserts. Sometimes that will be welcome, and sometimes you will not want that change. They can be used to sweeten plain yogurt or hot drinks. To use a liquid sweetener in a recipe that calls for a granulated sweetener, you will need to make some other changes. They cannot be substituted one for one, like you can do when switching one granulated sweetener for another. However, don't let this stop you from trying. It's not hard; it's just something you need to keep in mind.

Honey is sweeter than sugar, so you will want to use less. For every one cup of sugar called for in a recipe, use one half to two-thirds cup of honey. Because honey will be adding extra liquid to your recipe, you will want to decrease the other liquids. For every half cup of honey that you add, decrease the other liquids by a total of two tablespoons to one fourth cup. To substitute maple syrup for sugar, you will use two-thirds to three-fourths cup of maple syrup for every cup of sugar. Decrease the liquids in the

Energy Bites

Try these delicious little treats for an afternoon pick-me-up. They make a great after school snack! I like to use less sweetener when I make these for myself. My kids like them a bit sweeter, though.

1 cup old-fashioned or quick cooking oats

1/3 cup ground flaxseed

2/3 cup creamy peanut butter

3 tablespoons to ¼ cup honey

1 teaspoon vanilla extract

1/8 teaspoon salt

¼ cup mini chocolate chips

1. Add the oats to the bowl of a food processor or blender and pulse until they become small pieces.

2. Add the flaxseed, peanut butter, honey, vanilla extract, and salt. Process until the ingredients come together into a large ball.

3. Remove from the food processor and put into a large bowl. Add the mini chocolate chips and mix them in with a wooden spoon.

4. Using a small cookie scoop or a teaspoon, break off small chunks from the batter and roll into balls. Place on a cookie sheet or plate.

5. Refrigerate for 20 minutes to help the energy bites firm up.

You can replace the chocolate chips with other mix-ins if you'd like. Some ideas include shredded coconut, nuts, or dried fruit. Try some new combinations!

Homemade Granola Bars

These are healthy little desserts for after lunch. They can even be added to breakfast. To make them fun and colorful, my kids really like when I add mini M&M's.

2 ½ cups quick oats (or 1 ½ cups quick oats and 1 cup old-fashioned oats)

½ cup crisp rice cereal

¼ cup shredded coconut

½ cup mix-ins, such as dried fruit, chopped nuts, mini chocolate chips, peanut butter chips, mini M&M's

¼ cup plus 2 tablespoons coconut sugar or brown sugar

½ teaspoon salt

½ cup butter (1 stick), softened

¼ cup honey

½ teaspoon vanilla

1. Add the oats, cereal, shredded coconut, and mix-ins in a large bowl and mix together.

2. In a saucepan, add the sugar, salt, butter, and honey. Heat until the butter is melted and ingredients are warm, but not boiling. Remove from heat and add the vanilla.

3. Pour the wet ingredients in the sauce pan over the dry ingredients. Mix together well with a wooden spoon.

4. Press into a lightly greased 7- by 11-inch pan. This needs to be pressed down tightly so that they will stick together. I use a piece of wax paper on top and push down with my hands.

5. Let the bars completely cool before cutting and separating into bars. These can be put into the refrigerator to cool them down more quickly.

Chocolate Fudge
Sour Cream Bundt Cake

This cake is delicious! Don't let the longer list of ingredients scare you off. It's not too difficult and makes an elegant dessert. This one is great after a family dinner, but it's also nice enough to serve to company.

For the Pan:

2 tablespoons butter, melted

2 tablespoons cocoa powder

For the Cake:

1 cup butter (2 sticks)

1/3 cup natural, unsweetened cocoa powder

½ teaspoon salt

1 cup water

1 ¾ cup flour (I use freshly ground soft white wheat)

1 ½ cups granulated sweetener

1 ½ teaspoons baking soda

2 large eggs

¾ cup sour cream

1 teaspoon vanilla extract

1 to 2 cups semisweet chocolate chips

For the Glaze:

1 cup semisweet chocolate chips

2/3 cup heavy whipping cream

¼ teaspoon vanilla

1. Preheat the oven to 350 degrees F.

2. In a small bowl, mix together the butter and cocoa powder for the pan until it is well-combined and pasty. Use a pastry brush or square of wax paper to wipe the mixture into a 10- or 12-inch Bundt pan until the inner surface is evenly coated.

3. In a medium saucepan, combine the butter, cocoa powder, salt, and water. Heat until the butter is melted and whisk to combine well. Set aside to cool to about room temperature.

4. In a large bowl, whisk together the flour, sweetener, and baking soda. Pour in the chocolate mixture and stir to combine.

5. Add the eggs and whisk to combine. Stir in the sour cream and vanilla extract until the batter is smooth. Fold in the chocolate chips.

6. Spread the batter evenly in the prepared pan and bake for 40 to 45 minutes until the top lightly springs back and the cake is baked through.

7. Let the cake cool for five to 10 minutes in the pan before turning it out carefully onto a cooling rack to cool completely.

8. For the glaze, place the chocolate chips in a medium bowl. Heat the cream to a simmer (either in the microwave or on the stovetop) and pour over the chocolate chips. Let the mixture sit for a few minutes without stirring. Add the vanilla and stir the mixture until it is glossy and smooth. The

glaze will become firmer as it cools; if you want a thin drizzle, pour it over the cake while the glaze is still warm, but if you want a thicker frosting, let it cool slightly.

9. Once the cake is cooled, place it on a serving plate or cake stand and pour the glaze over the cake, letting it drip down the sides.

Recipe adapted with permission from Mel's Kitchen Cafe. For the original recipe, please visit www.melskitchencafe.com/chocolate-fudge-sour-cream-bundt-cake/.

Oatmeal Chocolate Chip Cookies

These might be my favorite cookies! They aren't too sweet and they only spread a little bit. I like thick, chewy cookies. If you prefer them flatter, you can flatten them out a little bit before baking them.

1 cup butter, softened

½ cup coconut sugar or brown sugar

½ cup (scant) granulated sweetener

2 eggs

2 teaspoons vanilla extract

1 ¼ cups flour (I use freshly milled soft white wheat)

½ teaspoon baking soda

1 teaspoon salt

3 cups old-fashioned oats

1 cup chopped walnuts

1 cup mini chocolate chips

1. Preheat the oven to 325 degrees F.

2. Cream the butter and both sugars together with a mixer in a large bowl until smooth. Add the eggs one at a time. Add vanilla extract.

3. In a medium bowl, whisk together the flour, baking soda, and salt.

4. Add the dry ingredients to the large bowl and stir together with a wooden spoon. Mix in the oats, walnuts, and chocolate chips.

5. Drop by heaping tablespoons on an ungreased baking sheet or a sheet lined with a silicone mat.

6. Bake for 10 to 12 minutes. Remove as soon as the edges of the cookies begin to brown. Let cool. Store in an airtight container.

Chapter 9
Spice Mixes, Condiments, and Sauces Made Easy

Many people buy bottled condiments or sauces and envelopes of spice mixes at the grocery store because it's convenient. However, these premade sauces almost always contain extra ingredients and preservatives that you probably don't want to be consuming on a regular basis. If I told you that it isn't much harder to mix your own from common ingredients in your home, than it is to stroll through the aisles at the grocery store hunting down bottles or envelopes, would you be willing to give it a try?

In addition to avoiding unwanted ingredients, another huge benefit of making your own mixes and condiments is the taste. The taste of homemade sauces and spice mixes just cannot be paralleled by something already packaged and sitting on a shelf at the store.

Spice Mixes

These dry spice mixes can be mixed ahead of time and kept in a jar in your cupboard. They only take minutes to create. They can be used the same way as an envelope of spice mix from the store. In chapter seven, I showed you how you can make a large batch of ranch dressing mix and also Italian dressing mix. Obviously, these can be used to make salad dressings. They can also be used in any recipe that calls for an envelope of ranch dressing mix or Italian dressing mix. Just substitute two tablespoons of your homemade dressing mix for one envelope.

Some other easy mixes that only take a few minutes to make include taco seasoning and onion soup mix. These can be used just as you would their envelope counterparts, substituting two tablespoons of homemade mix for one envelope of store-bought mix.

Condiments and Sauces

Some easy condiments that can be made in your own kitchen include taco sauce, barbecue sauce, and pizza sauce. These can be made ahead of time and frozen, or you can just throw them together while your taco meat is browning or your chicken is roasting. It's very easy. As long as you have included them in your meal plan for the week and listed the ingredients on your shopping list, you will have everything you need to make them. They only take a couple of minutes to put together. I typically make a large batch of pizza sauce and freeze whatever I'm not using that day in zipper-topped bags. I make taco sauce and barbecue sauce the day I need it. If I have leftovers, I freeze them in bags. They just take a few minutes to thaw out in hot water as the rest of your meal is cooking.

Give these sauces and spice mixes a try. You'll love them and you won't ever want store-bought mixes again.

Steps to Improving Condiments, Sauces, and Spice Mixes

1. Pick one of the following spice mix recipes and make a large batch for your spice cabinet. (Can I recommend the taco seasoning? It's awesome!) Add two tablespoons of the mix to each pound of ground beef as you're browning it. Once your jar is running low, add any spices you'll need to your shopping list and make up a new batch when you have a couple of minutes. Doing this before you need it in your meal is such a huge help. You won't have to think about it when you're trying to get dinner on the table in a hurry.

2. Add more spice mixes when you feel ready. Make sure that you label your jars so you remember which spice mix is which!

3. Try making sauce from scratch the next time you're making tacos or pizza. For the following pizza sauce recipe, you'll need to put the ingredients into your crockpot earlier in the day so it's ready when you have your dough rolled out. For taco sauce, you can just dump everything into a small pan on the stove while your taco meat is browning. It just needs to simmer for a few minutes.

Homemade Pizza Sauce
in the Slow Cooker

This pizza sauce is so easy to throw together and is the best pizza sauce I've ever made! Let your slow cooker do the work for you. Add all the ingredients to your slow cooker in the morning. It will be cooled and ready to use by the time your dough is done in the evening. Pizza doesn't have to be difficult. This batch will make enough for about five pizzas.

4 six-oz. cans tomato paste

1 15-oz. can tomato sauce

1 cup water

1 teaspoon garlic powder

1 teaspoon onion powder

2 tablespoons Italian seasoning

1 teaspoon salt

½ teaspoon garlic powder

3 tablespoons olive or avocado oil

1 tablespoon honey

4 tablespoons Parmesan cheese

1. Add all of the ingredients, except the Parmesan cheese, to the slow cooker and stir to combine.

2. Cover and cook on low for four hours, stirring every 30 to 60 minutes so that it doesn't stick to the cooker.

3. After four hours, add the Parmesan cheese and stir to combine.

4. Cool to room temperature.

5. Use in the next day or two, or package and freeze. To freeze, add one scant cup of sauce to a zipper-top bag. Remove excess air, label, and freeze.

Recipe used with permission from Humorous Homemaking. For the original recipe, please visit www.humoroushomemaking.com/fix-and-forget-friday-crock-pot-pizza-sauce.

Taco Seasoning

This is one of my favorite spice mixes to have on hand. I use it for taco meat and sometimes I add it to chili or a taco dip that I make. It is so much better than the envelopes of seasoning. Try it with mashed avocadoes for a quick and yummy guacamole, too.

½ cup chili powder

¼ cup onion powder

2 tablespoons ground cumin

1 tablespoon garlic powder

1 tablespoon paprika

1 tablespoon sea salt

1. Add all the spices to a jar or other container with a lid.

2. Shake until well-mixed.

3. Label and store in the pantry or spice cabinet.

4. Shake before each use to ensure all of the spices are evenly distributed. Use two tablespoons for each pound of ground beef for taco meat.

Onion Soup Mix

2/3 cup dried minced onion

3 teaspoons dried parsley flakes

2 teaspoons onion powder

1 teaspoon celery salt

1 teaspoon sea salt

1 teaspoon granulated sweetener

½ teaspoon ground black powder

1. Add all spices to a jar or other container with a lid.

2. Shake until evenly mixed.

3. Label and store in pantry or spice cabinet.

4. Shake before each use to ensure that all the spices are evenly distributed.

5. Use two to four tablespoons to replace one envelope of seasoning. I usually use two, but if you find your recipe needs more flavor, then increase to four tablespoons.

Homemade Barbecue Sauce

¾ cup ketchup (Try to find a brand that contains little to no sweetener, or experiment with making your own.)

1 teaspoon onion powder

¼ teaspoon garlic powder

1 teaspoon liquid smoke

1 tablespoon honey (This is optional, for a honey barbecue taste.)

Mix all ingredients in a small saucepan. Heat on low for five to 10 minutes. Cool and serve.

Chapter 10
Proteins

I'm guessing that most of the time, when you think about adding protein to your meal, you think about meat. That's the most common protein. Other common proteins include beans and legumes, fish, nuts, and eggs. All of these are great sources of healthy proteins and can be added to any meal or snack to make it heartier. I have personally found that eating a protein along with carbohydrates helps to curb the blood sugar spikes and drops. If you struggle with feeling hungry, or just "off," soon after eating a carb-heavy snack or meal, try pairing it with a protein and see if that helps.

If you remember from chapter three, proteins are made up of amino acids. If we eat a food or combination of foods that contain all the essential amino acids, it's called a "complete protein." Other than the common proteins, grains and vegetables also have protein. Gluten is actually a protein. These amino acids can be combined in various ways to form what is called a complete protein. This is why rice and beans are often served together. They make a complete protein. Vegetarians use these types of combinations in their meals to ensure they are receiving the proper amounts of protein.

Purchasing Meat

It's harder to find and more expensive to purchase meats that have been raised on appropriate diets, not exposed to genetically modified organisms, and not full of antibiotics. Often, local farmers will have high-quality meats that they sell for less than you can find in a grocery store. It is worth researching. Typically, you can purchase the beef from a whole cow, a half cow, or a quarter cow. You can also specify the type of cuts you want. Our family eats a lot of ground beef, so when I order from a local farmer, I ask to get most of the beef ground. I will also get a couple of roasts and some stew meat. The ground beef comes in one pound packages. I put all of this into an upright freezer and thaw it as needed.

Chicken, turkey, eggs, and pork can also be purchased locally. These, too, can be processed in different ways, including whole chickens or turkeys ready for Thanksgiving.

There will be times when you'll purchase your meats from your grocery store. Buying from a local farmer isn't always possible. Or, you may run out of meat before the farmer has more animals ready for processing. Maybe you don't have a freezer to store all that meat in. In that case, buy the best that you can find and afford and don't worry about it.

Buying the best meats available will put a huge dent in your grocery budget. Depending on the size of your budget, this may not be possible. If you're concerned about the quality of your meats, buy some of your weekly meat in higher quality and the rest in lower quality. You might also consider eating less meat by serving more vegetarian meals and incorporating other good sources of proteins.

Other Protein Sources

Other than meat, eggs and beans are great sources of protein that can be included in a healthy diet. I often boil several eggs at the beginning of the week and keep them in my refrigerator for easy breakfast additions—or any meal, really. If you want to protect your budget, or have more control over what's in your food, making beans at home is very simple.

You can make a large batch of beans and package them into bags with about two cups in each bag, flatten the bag, and store them in your freezer. Each bag can be used to replace one can of beans. You will find specific directions for making a large batch of beans, as well as my go-to method for making hardboiled eggs in a pressure cooker in the recipes section of this chapter. You can make both of these recipes with a standard pot on the stove if you don't yet own a pressure cooker.

A fun, easy snack that is high in protein and kid-friendly is trail mix. To make this, all you need to do is pour the various ingredients into a large bowl, stir them up, and serve it or package it in small portions to save for later. Trail mix includes nuts and seeds—which make this a high-protein snack—and dried foods. Add at least one ingredient that is high in protein. We'll often add chocolate chips to ours. This isn't the healthiest route, but it definitely increases the yum factor and helps ensure my kids will eat it. You can also add popcorn if you want. Just choose the types of nuts, seeds, and fruits that your family enjoys and mix them together. It couldn't get any easier!

Steps to Improving Your Proteins

1. Evaluate whether purchasing beef, chicken, or other meats or eggs from a local farmer is an option for you. If so, contact the farmer and place your order. It often takes a while from the time you order to when you're able to pick up the meat, so planning ahead is imperative.

2. Consult your budget and decide how much more money, if any, you want to devote to purchasing higher quality meats from the grocery store. If this is not feasible right now, then please do not stress about it. Just get the best that you can.

3. Make tacos. Tacos are a great way to incorporate your homemade taco seasoning from chapter nine, as well as fresh produce like lettuce, tomatoes, and avocadoes. We love taco Tuesdays!

4. Make a batch of hardboiled eggs to keep in your refrigerator and grab them as needed throughout the week.

5. Make a pot of beans and divide the cooked beans into two-cup portions to freeze for later use. Consider serving them with rice for a complete protein. While rice is not a protein, I have included my favorite method for making rice in the pressure cooker in this chapter. If you don't have one, I recommend saving up to get one. Serve rice and beans together for a complete protein.

Tacos in the Oven

I enjoy making tacos in the oven these days. It seems to make it easier and quicker to serve them. Consider using the taco seasoning from chapter nine. This is one of our favorite meals!

1 lb. ground beef

2 tablespoons homemade taco seasoning

18 – 24 hard taco shells

2 cups or 1 can black beans, rinsed and dried

2 cups Colby Jack cheese, shredded

Include toppings of your choice, such as shredded lettuce, diced tomatoes, avocado, sour cream, and taco sauce.

1. Preheat the oven to 350 degrees F.

2. Brown the ground beef with the taco seasoning.

3. Stand the taco shells up in two pans. I usually use one 9- by 13-inch pan and one 7- by 11-inch pan. Fit them in as close as possible so that they don't fall over.

4. Mix the black beans into the cooked ground beef.

Magically Moist Chicken

This recipe comes from my grandma. The title is not an exaggeration! This chicken comes out so tender and moist. This may be my family's favorite way to eat chicken.

4 boneless, skinless chicken breasts

½ cup mayonnaise

1 ¼ cups bread crumbs (Add a few slices of bread to a food processor and process until you have small crumbs.)

1. Preheat the oven to 425 degrees F.

2. Using a pastry brush, brush the mayonnaise onto both sides of the chicken breasts.

3. Coat the chicken with bread crumbs. I find this is easiest by putting the bread crumbs into a pie plate and laying the coated chicken breast on the crumbs and then flipping it over to cover the whole thing.

4. Lay the chicken onto a baking pan.

5. Cook in preheated oven for 20 minutes, or until chicken is thoroughly cooked all the way through.

Hardboiled Eggs in the Pressure Cooker

Boiling eggs in an electric pressure cooker is easy, quick, and produces hardboiled eggs with shells that peel off easily. Hardboiled eggs are a great recipe to try if you are new to using an electric pressure cooker.

Use as many eggs as you want to make and can fit in a single layer in the bottom of your pressure cooker.

1 ½ cup water

1. Place the metal trivet or rack in the bottom of the pressure cooker pot.

2. Gently lay the eggs on the tray, keeping them in a single layer. It does not take any longer to do more eggs, so add as many or as few as you like.

3. Pour the 1 ½ cups of water into the pressure cooker pot.

4. Seal the lid and set the timer to seven minutes on high pressure.

5. While the eggs are cooking, fill a bowl with water and ice.

6. Release the pressure manually when the seven minutes are over.

7. Using tongs, remove the eggs and place them into the ice water to stop the cooking.

8. Once cool, crack the shell and peel it off. It should slip off easily.

Black Beans in the Pressure Cooker

Cooking beans in the pressure cooker is a lot quicker than on the stovetop. It's cheaper to cook dried beans yourself than to buy cans, so this can be a help to your budget. I don't usually soak my beans ahead of time and we haven't noticed any difference in the final result. This method is the same for other types of beans, but the cooking time may vary. Many pressure cooker cookbooks include a time chart showing how long to cook different types of beans. Visit *homeandfaith.com/resources* for some of my favorite cookbooks.

1 lb. black beans

8 cups water

1 tablespoon oil

2 cloves of garlic, optional

1 bay leaf, optional

¼ of an onion, optional

1 teaspoon salt, optional

1. Rinse the beans and pick through them, removing any small stones you may find. Put the beans in the bottom of the pressure cooker pot.

2. Pour the water in and add the oil.

3. Add any or all of the optional seasonings.

4. Seal the lid and set the timer for 24 minutes on high.

5. Allow the pressure to release naturally. Foam will develop as the beans cook. Manually releasing the pressure will allow the foam to spit and spray out. You can avoid this by allowing the pressure to release naturally.

I like to bag up whatever I'm not using right away in two-cup portions and freeze for future use.

If you prefer, you can soak your beans by covering them with water in a bowl. Let them sit overnight. Drain the water and proceed with the steps above, changing the cook time to six minutes, and allow the pressure to release naturally.

Rice in the Pressure Cooker

Rice is a grain, but I have included it here in the chapter about proteins because when combined with beans, this makes a complete protein. This method of cooking rice is so easy and always turns out perfectly cooked, delicious rice.

2 cups rice (I like Jasmine Rice)

3 cups chicken broth (can substitute water, but the rice will be less flavorful)

½ teaspoon salt

1. Place the rice in the bottom of the pressure cooker.

2. Add the chicken broth.

3. Sprinkle salt on top.

4. Seal the pressure cooker and set it to cook on high for three minutes. After it has finished cooking, allow the pressure to release naturally for 10 minutes. If there is any pressure remaining after 10 minutes, release the pressure manually.

5. Fluff the rice and serve.

Chapter 11
Healthy Fats

Everyone knows fats are not healthy, right? I'm trying to get rid of fat, not add it!

Well, not exactly. Some fats are unhealthy and will go straight to your waistline as well as your arteries and other places that you don't want them. However, there is such a thing as healthy fat. Our bodies need some fat. Fat is essentially stored energy. We rely on this when we're not getting enough energy from other sources. When we eat more calories than we use up, these extra calories are stored as fat.

Do I Really Need Fat?

Our nerve cells are coated in a layer of fat called the myelin sheath. This allows messages to be transmitted from one cell to the next. Our brain absolutely needs an adequate amount of fat in order to function properly and send messages to other parts of the body. All the cells in our bodies contain fat in the membrane. The membrane controls the flow in and out of the cell.

Fat is also used to transport vitamins through our bloodstream. For example, vitamins A, D, E, and K are fat-soluble. They require fat in order to be usable. Fat is used to regulate many other bodily processes, such as the production of hormones.

So, as you can see, a fat-free diet will not be helpful. You may lose weight at first, but you will sacrifice other important and necessary functions. Eventually your body will start to hoard whatever bits of fat that do make their way into your body and will store them up. Your initial weight loss will not last. It is much easier on your body, and much healthier, not to avoid fat, but to eat the right kind and the right amount of fats.

What Kinds of Fat Should I Consume?

Just to review, saturated fats come mostly from animal sources such as meat, dairy products like cheese, milk, butter, and eggs. Coconut and palm oils are also sources of saturated fat, even though they come from plant sources. About half of our cell membranes are made from saturated fats.

Typically, unsaturated fats come from plant sources. Some examples include olive oil, avocados, and peanuts. Our cell membranes need some unsaturated fats just like they need saturated fats.

Trans fats are mostly artificial fats. They are made by altering the state of a fat by changing its chemical structure. These are used in fried foods at fast food restaurants and processed goods in the grocery stores, like cookies.

I think it's pretty easy to tell which of these fats should be avoided. Trans fats are generally unhealthy and should be replaced with healthier options. Both saturated and unsaturated fats are present in the food that God created for us. Trans fats are made in a factory. I'm not advocating that we should *never* splurge on a quick treat at the grocery store, or that something catastrophic will happen if we go to a drive-through every now and then.

Remember, we are giving ourselves the grace we need to do the best we can in all areas of our lives without adding a layer of guilt or a sense of failure around our decisions. Sometimes that means we're spending our time and energy on something other than the kitchen and we just need to do something easy. However, if this is becoming a regular habit, then our priorities need to be evaluated. Of course, the priorities you choose for you and your family may look very different from what I have decided for mine.

Balance is Key

There is a lot of conflicting information about which fats are healthy or whether we should avoid them altogether. (By the way, fat-free foods have excess sugar and fillers to replace the fat that was removed from the food. Fats provide flavor and something must be added to make it appealing when fat has been removed. Remember that excess sugar in the body ends up stored in our fat cells.)

One thing to keep in mind is that many studies that are used to back up various nutritional claims were conducted and financially sponsored by companies or groups that have much to gain or lose by the results of the study. I'm not trying to start conspiracy theories; I'm just reminding you to look at the results of these studies critically.

Statistics and studies can be manipulated to prove anything you want them to prove. I am counting on the fact that God knew what He was doing when He gave us our food. I am not relying on scientists to tell me what I should or should not eat. I am also relying on the fact that God made a wonderful creation when He made our bodies; able to heal itself and handle a diet that is not 100 percent perfect at all times. I eat my less-than-stellar treats now and then and I balance them with delicious, nutrient-dense foods the rest of the time.

Healthy Fats

It is actually much easier than you're probably imagining to use healthy fats in your kitchen. I use five main sources for fats in my recipes. For liquid fats, I use either olive oil, avocado oil, or melted coconut oil. I am not a huge fan of the way olive oil tastes, so more often than not, I use avocado oil. For a solid fat I use coconut oil, butter, or palm shortening.

Coconut oil can be used as either a liquid or a solid fat. It will turn to liquid at 76 degrees. So, gently heating your coconut oil will provide you with a liquid oil. Unrefined coconut oil has a mild coconut taste, making it a perfect oil for sweet baked goods, like cookies and cakes or quick breads. Refined coconut oil has no flavor and can be used in dishes in which you don't want to impart a coconut flavor. Palm shortening is a perfect replacement for other shortenings commonly sold in supermarkets.

For each of these oils, just replace whatever is called for in the recipe one for one. If a recipe calls for a half cup of margarine, you can just use a half cup of butter or coconut oil. For some specific recommendations on the exact products that I use regularly in my kitchen, please visit my website at *homeandfaith.com/resources*.

Steps to Improving Fats

1. Replace margarine with butter.

2. Purchase coconut oil to replace other solid fats in recipes. You could also use butter.

3. Replace vegetable oils with olive or avocado oil.

4. Replace shortenings with palm shortening or coconut oil.

Whole Wheat Pie Crust

If you are scared to make homemade pie crust, then this recipe is for you. It is easy and I have never had it turn out badly. Your family will thank you!

1 ¼ cup freshly ground soft white wheat flour

¼ teaspoon salt

1/3 cup palm shortening

4-5 tablespoons cold water

1. Preheat the oven to 450 degrees F.

2. Add the flour, salt, and palm shortening to the bowl of a food processor. Process until the mixture looks like small crumbs.

3. Add four tablespoons of water and continue processing. If the mixture doesn't come together in a nice ball, then add more water (1/2 teaspoon at a time) until it forms a ball.

4. Remove the ball of dough to a generously floured surface. I like to use a pastry mat with measured circles printed on it.

5. Roll the dough into a circle to fit in your pie plate, adding more flour to the dough and rolling pin as needed.

6. Carefully transfer the crust to your pie plate. I typically do this by gently wrapping the floured dough around my rolling pin and then unrolling it onto the pie plate.

7. Using a fork, poke a few holes in the bottom of the crust. This helps to keep air bubbles from forming in the crust as it bakes.

8. Bake in the preheated oven for about 10 minutes, or until the crust is golden brown.

Fat Bombs

This a great afternoon pick-me-up. It is so easy; even your little kids can help make this. They'll love to help eat it, too!

½ cup coconut oil

½ cup peanut butter

¼ cup cocoa powder

¼ cup raw honey

½ teaspoon vanilla

Dash of salt

1. Melt the coconut oil. Combine the oil with the peanut butter in a medium-sized bowl. Whisk together until smooth, with no peanut butter lumps.

2. Stir in the cocoa powder, honey, vanilla, and salt.

3. Line a baking pan with parchment paper or a silicone mat and pour the peanut butter mixture on it.

4. Use a spatula to carefully spread it out smoothly.

5. Sprinkle with another dash of salt if you like.

6. Refrigerate until firm and then break it into pieces.

7. Store in the refrigerator or freezer. Because coconut oil melts at 76 degrees, this will get very soft if left at room temperature for too long.

Recipe used with permission from Humorous Homemaking. For the original recipe, please visit www.humoroushomemaking.com/peanut-butter-fat-bombs.

Chapter 12
Odds and Ends

We have covered a lot of ground so far! In this last chapter, we'll discuss a few final ideas that will help in your kitchen when it comes to improving the health of your family.

Beverages

Let's talk about drinks. What do you drink most of the time? Before my third child was born, I drank soda all . . . the . . . time. I couldn't stand the taste of water and would rather not have a drink at all than drink water. However, late in this third pregnancy, the baby's heart was beating really fast during one of my appointments. The doctor ordered a non-stress test. Over the course of that test, her heart rate settled back down. The doctor felt okay about these results, but I left with strict orders to not drink any soda or juice. The sugar and possible caffeine could impact the baby and elevate her heart rate back to those dangerous levels. This was all the motivation I needed. I gave up my habit cold turkey.

We ordered water to be delivered in big jugs that sit on a water cooler. As long as I had this filtered water, as long as it had absolutely no taste, and as long as it was always ice cold right out of the spigot, I could drink it. It wasn't easy because I still craved soda. Actually, I still do. Anytime I hear the metallic pop and fizz of someone opening a soda can, I start to salivate. I love soda.

I didn't drink anything on the "black list" for the rest of my pregnancy. After she was born, I did relax my standards a bit and had a soda every now and then, but I've never gone back to caffeinated sodas. I don't keep it in my house, because I know I'll have no self-restraint. I'll drink it until it's gone.

Caffeine

Many people love to drink coffee. They love the taste as well as its ability to stimulate the body. Caffeine is a natural substance in coffee and also in many teas. It's responsible for that boost of energy you get after drinking a cup of Joe, and it can stay in your body for four to six hours. Chocolate, energy drinks, and many sodas also contain caffeine.

While caffeine is legal, it is considered a stimulant. It affects your central nervous system when consumed. It can be addictive, and quitting can lead to withdrawal symptoms, such as headaches and fatigue. You can also build up a tolerance to caffeine, meaning that it will take more caffeine to give you the effect you want.

Caffeine consumption has pros and cons. You will have to decide for yourself whether you want to drink caffeinated beverages, and how much to drink. Some positive effects of caffeine are that it can temporarily improve your mood. Also, as previously mentioned, it can give you an increase in energy.

Some negative effects of caffeine include anxiety and insomnia, especially in high amounts (about four cups of coffee or more). It can also cause an irregular heartbeat and may inhibit calcium from being absorbed by the bones.

Water

Maybe your drink of choice isn't soda. Maybe you love coffee or tea. Or maybe it's lemonade. Whatever it is, it's important that it be well-balanced with water. The majority of your liquid intake should be plain water. Some say you should have eight servings or eight ounces of water every day for a total of 64 ounces. Others say you should drink half your body weight in ounces each day. For example, if you weigh 150 pounds, then you should drink half of that, or 75 ounces daily. This makes more sense to me, because it stands to reason that a bigger person needs more water than a smaller person, right?

To ensure that I'm getting enough each day, I keep track of how much water I've been drinking. I keep a small card on my kitchen counter and mark off a section each time whenever I drink eight ounces. This is a great visual reminder of how much I've already had and how much more I need to drink.

If you are not used to drinking much water, increase your intake slowly so that you do not stress your body out. Try adding an extra eight ounces each week until you have reached your target amount. This slow increase will help your body adjust to the additional fluids more gently.

In developed countries, water is cleaned and considered safe to drink and cook with straight out of the faucet. Often, fluoride is added to tap water.

Mineral water comes from a natural source, such as a spring. It usually has a high level of minerals in it. Today, this water is often bottled and sold in stores.

Many people prefer bottled water. Bottled water doesn't always come from a natural source. It may be the same as tap water. Check the manufacturer of your preferred bottled water to find out the source.

Creating a Healthy Gut

Did you know that your body is full of billions of microorganisms? A gut that is functioning properly is full of healthy bacteria called probiotics. If your gut becomes overrun with yeast, this will crowd out the probiotics and leave us with many undesirable side effects which can range from achy joints and fatigue to yeast infections. You can support your own gut by adding probiotics to your diet.

Probiotics are found in foods such as yogurt and kefir, which are forms of fermented dairy. They are also found in other fermented foods like sauerkraut and fermented pickles. If you do not have easy access, or you don't like these foods, then taking a probiotic supplement can help.

Making yogurt and kefir at home is very easy to do. Kefir just takes a couple of minutes to make and can be added to smoothies if your family doesn't like the taste of it straight from a cup. Yogurt doesn't take much hands-on time, but it does take the whole day to complete. You don't have to be home for most of it, though. I sometimes make yogurt in the pressure cooker, of course! This is our favorite yogurt, but like everything else, when life is busy, we buy yogurt from the store and eat it happily.

How or when you implement these changes is entirely up to you. These are easy alterations and often make a noticeable difference pretty quickly in how you feel. Try it and see!

Chapter 13
Conclusion

You've made it to the end! That was a lot of information, wasn't it? I hope you learned a few things and feel excited to jump in and start transforming your cooking for the better. I hope you don't feel overwhelmed, but instead empowered. I hope you don't feel stressed. Rather, I hope you feel protected by grace.

You have undoubtedly come into contact with many well-meaning food "experts" who have offered their advise on all types of eating plans and styles. It is so easy to read this information, much of it conflicting, and not know which direction to head. At the same time, we want to be healthier and help our children to establish healthy patterns of living while they are still young.

I do not believe that Jesus wanted us to feel stressed and overwhelmed by our responsibilities. After all, He said, "I have come to give life, and give it abundantly." I think He saw living abundantly as having full lives that are wonderful and fulfilling.

If we are listening and obeying what He is asking us to do, then life should not be full of guilt and frustration. We should be able to rest in Him and know that He leads us only to what He knows is best for us. That doesn't mean it will be easy and pain-free, but it will be full of peace that only He can give and grace that only He can cover us with.

The bottom line is that you do not want to avoid any certain food group. They are all important and each adds its own benefits and fulfills its own purpose toward helping us have fully-functioning, healthy bodies. As you eat and feed your family, pay attention to how you feel. For example, if you feel less energetic after a carb-heavy meal, then you may want to consider decreasing, but not eliminating, carbs at that time of day and increase your protein and fat intake. By paying attention to the feedback that your body gives you, you will be able to make small changes to your diet.

Another important area to pay attention to is when you feel hungry and when you feel full. Often, we get so busy in our days that we may forget to stop and eat! Or, we may be so busy talking to the family that we eat everything on our plates even though we felt satisfied several minutes and spoonfuls ago. We begin to tune out these signals that our body is designed to send us. By not eating when we are hungry, we allow our blood sugar to continue to drop, sending it on a roller coaster ride when we do decide to eat. When we don't stop eating after we feel full, our portion sizes become too large. This can lead to weight gain.

The goal should be to eat when we are hungry and stop as soon as we feel like we've had enough. It is not necessary to clean your plate. Also, purposefully skipping snacks or even meals, when you are truly hungry is not healthy, either. You need to keep your blood sugar as stable as possible, with only minor dips and rises throughout the day. This can happen by simply paying closer attention to how you feel throughout the day.

It is important to repeat that you will not want to make all of the changes mentioned throughout this book in one day or even one month. And, it is not necessary. To truly transform your cooking, and inevitably your health, you need to make small, but sustainable changes. This is how you make real and lasting lifestyle changes. By attempting too much, too quickly, you will lose steam and give up. But, by incorporating one small change at a time and continuing it until you are very comfortable with it, you will change your cooking. You will be able to maintain the changes. By giving yourself permission to move slowly and comfortably, you are giving yourself the same grace that God gives you.

Take your changes in the kitchen one step at a time and know that you are doing awesome things for yourself and your family. Serve those meals with a smile on your face. You can do it!

Made in the USA
San Bernardino, CA
02 December 2018